Steck-Vaughn

Language Exercises

Book 7

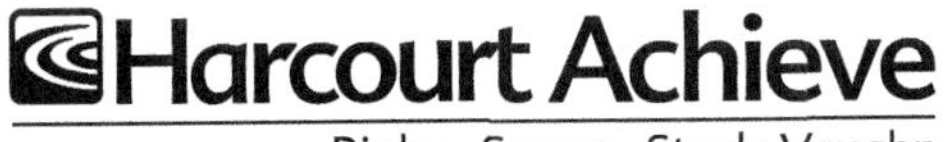

www.HarcourtAchieve.com
1.800.531.5015

Acknowledgments

Macmillan/McGraw-Hill School Publishing Company: Pronunciation Key, reprinted with permission of the publisher, from *Macmillan School Dictionary 1.* Copyright © 1990 Macmillan Publishing Company, a division of Macmillan, Inc.

LANGUAGE EXERCISES Series:

Book 1	Book 4	Book 7
Book 2	Book 5	Book 8
Book 3	Book 6	Review

ISBN 978-1-4190-1875-6 ISBN 1-4190-1875-2

9 10 2266 18 17 16 4500585059
Printed in the United States of America

Table of Contents

Unit 6 Study Skills

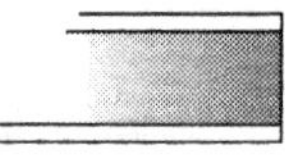

Final Reviews

Check What You Know

A. Write S before each pair of synonyms, A before each pair of antonyms, and H before each pair of homonyms.

_____ **1.** board, bored
_____ **2.** tall, short
_____ **3.** antique, ancient
_____ **4.** massive, huge

B. Write the homograph for the pair of meanings.

_____ **a.** a piece of hair **b.** to fasten securely

C. Write P before each word with a prefix, S before each word with a suffix, and C before each compound word.

_____ **1.** overcome
_____ **2.** misplace
_____ **3.** rusty
_____ **4.** disinterested

D. Write the words that make up each contraction.

_____ _____ **1.** they'll _____ _____ **2.** we've

E. Underline the word in parentheses that has the more positive connotation.

The (crabby, unhappy) child squirmed in her mother's arms.

F. Circle the number of the idiom that means to suddenly become angry.

1. put up with **2.** fly off the handle

G. Write D before the declarative sentence, IM before the imperative sentence, E before the exclamatory sentence, and IN before the interrogative sentence. Then underline the simple subject, and circle the simple predicate in each sentence.

_____ **1.** Wait until the speech is over.
_____ **2.** What do you believe?
_____ **3.** Ouch! I burned myself!
_____ **4.** That article really made me angry.

H. Write CS before the sentence that has a compound subject and CP before the sentence that has a compound predicate.

_____ **1.** He stumbled and fell on the rough ground.
_____ **2.** Carmen and José are the leading actors.

I. Write CS before the compound sentence. Write RO before the run-on sentence. Write I before the sentence that is in inverted order.

_____ **1.** Through the woods ran the frightened deer.
_____ **2.** Once she had lived in New York, she lives in Toronto now.
_____ **3.** Brenda was cold, so she built a roaring fire.

J. Put brackets ([ ]) around the subordinate clause, and underline the independent clause in this complex sentence. Then write DO above the direct object.

After I moved into town, I rented a beautiful new apartment.

K. Underline the common nouns, and circle the proper nouns in the sentence.

Mayor Dumonte showed the citizens of our city that he was honest by appointing Ms. Lopez to the position.

L. Circle the appositive in the sentence. Underline the noun it identifies or explains.

His favorite nurse, Ms. Abram, made his stay in the hospital more pleasant.

M. Write past, present, or future to show the tense of each underlined verb.

______ 1. We will have the best seats in the house.

______ 2. The actors prepare for months beforehand.

______ 3. Critics described this play as one of the best ever.

N. Circle the correct verbs in each sentence.

1. Here (is, are) the paper clips you (were, was) asking for.
2. She (seen, saw) her brother before he (know, knew) she was there.
3. It had (begun, began) to rain, so he (gone, went) inside.
4. She (thrown, threw) the dish and (broken, broke) it.

O. Circle the number of the sentence that is in the active voice.

1. The letter was received a day late.
2. Jerry sent his package in overnight mail.

P. Write SP before the sentence that has a subject pronoun, OP before the sentence that has an object pronoun, PP before the sentence that has a possessive pronoun, and IP before the sentence that has an indefinite pronoun. Circle the pronoun in each sentence.

______ 1. Somebody knows what happened.

______ 2. Rick wrote that poem for her.

______ 3. The band played their favorite song.

______ 4. We felt surprised and upset.

Q. Underline the pronoun. Circle its antecedent.

The jets flew in their assigned formation.

R. On the line before each sentence, write adjective or adverb to describe the underlined word.

______ 1. That farm is up for sale.

______ 2. The dog's yelps were extremely loud.

______ 3. She spoke more enthusiastically than anyone else.

______ 4. Some Mexican food is very spicy and hot.

S. Underline each prepositional phrase twice. Circle each preposition. Underline the conjunction once.

The girl on the bus waved at me.

T. Rewrite the letter. Add capital letters and punctuation where needed.

956 e. garden circle
bowman tx 78787
april 13 2006

dear steve

were so excited youre coming to visit ___ even little scott managed to say uncle steve visit which was pretty good for a child of only twenty two months wouldnt you agree ___ oh i want to be sure i have the information correct ___ please let me know as soon as possible if any of this is wrong flight 561 arrives at 310 P.M. may 22 2006 ___ see you then ___

your sister
amanda

____

____

____

____

____

____

____

____

____

____

____

U. Number the sentences in order, with the topic sentence first.

_____ 1. Then the wool is combed and formed into neat rolls.

_____ 2. Making wool thread by hand is a time-consuming art.

_____ 3. The spinner goes to work making thread after the wool is combed.

_____ 4. First, a sheep's wool is shaved off and cleaned.

V. Circle the number of the best interview question.

1. Is it your feeling that the city council's decision has failed the voters?
2. Why do you think that the mayor voted against the rest of the council?

Homework 11/30/2017

W. Rewrite the sentence below. Correct the errors in the sentence by following the proofreader's marks.

Although ^the decision to ~~to~~ close mayfield park was unpoplar, proved it to be the correct choise⊙

____

X. Use the dictionary entry to answer the questions.

jolly (jäl′ ē) *adj.* **1.** full of high spirits: joyous. **2.** expressing, suggesting, or inspiring gaiety: cheerful. [Middle English *joli*]

at; āpe; fär; câre; end; mē; it; īce; pîerce; hot; ōld, sông; fôrk; oil; out; up; ūse; rüle; pu̇ll; tûrn; chin; sing; shop; thin; this; hw in white; zh in treasure. The symbol ə stands for the unstressed vowel sound in about, taken, pencil, lemon, and circus.

1. What part of speech is the word jolly? adjective
2. Would jolly come before or after joust in the dictionary? before
3. Which language is in the history of the word jolly? middle english
4. Write the word for this respelling: (gā′ et ē). gaiety
5. Write jolly separated into syllables. Jol/ly

Y. Write the source from the box that you would use to find the information listed.

dictionary	card catalog	encyclopedia	atlas	*Readers' Guide*

Readers' Guide 1. where to find an article in a certain magazine

card catalog 2. where to locate a certain book

Atlas 3. a map of Europe

dictionary 4. the etymology of the word lieutenant

encyclopedia 5. an article on soapstone

Below is a list of the part of the sections on *Check What You Know* and the pages on which the skills in each section are taught. If you missed any questions, turn to the pages listed, and practice the skills. Then correct the problems you missed on *Check What You Know.*

Section	Practice Page
Unit 1	
A	5, 6
B	7
C	8, 9, 11
D	10
E	12
F	13
Unit 2	
G	18–20, 23
H	25, 26
I	24, 33, 35

Section	Practice Page
J	28, 30, 34
Unit 3	
K	41–45
L	48
M	49–53
N	55–61
O	65
P	66, 67
Q	68
R	69–73
S	74, 75, 77

Section	Practice Page
Unit 4	
T	82–90
Unit 5	
U	96–98
V	102, 103
W	104–105
Unit 6	
X	110–114
Y	116–127

Lesson 1 Synonyms and Antonyms

■ A **synonym** is a word that has the same or nearly the same meaning as one or more other words. EXAMPLES: reply – answer talk – speak

A. Write a synonym for each word below.

1. pleasant ______
2. enough ______
3. leave ______
4. inquire ______
5. fearless ______
6. artificial ______
7. famous ______
8. trade ______
9. house ______
10. nation ______
11. difficult ______
12. vacant ______

B. Write four sentences about recycling. In each sentence, use a synonym for the word in parentheses. Underline the synonym.

1. (packaging) ______
2. (waste) ______
3. (landfill) ______
4. (planet) ______

■ An **antonym** is a word that has the opposite meaning of another word. EXAMPLES: old – new bad – good

C. Write an antonym for each word below.

1. failure ______
2. absent ______
3. before ______
4. slow ______
5. all ______
6. forget ______
7. love ______
8. no ______
9. friend ______
10. always ______
11. light ______
12. forward ______

D. In each sentence, write an antonym for the word in parentheses that makes sense in the sentence.

1. Thao ran his hand along the (smooth) ______ surface of the wood.
2. He knew he would have to (stop) ______ sanding it.
3. Only after sanding would he be able to (destroy) ______ a table.
4. He would try to (forget) ______ not to sand it too much.

Homonyms

■ A **homonym** is a word that sounds the same as another word but has a different spelling and a different meaning.
EXAMPLES: aisle – I'll – isle flower – flour

A. Underline the correct homonym(s) in each sentence below.

1. The (two, too, to) people walked very slowly (passed, past) the house.
2. The children were (two, too, to) tired (two, too, to) talk.
3. Did you (hear, here) that noise?
4. Yes, I (heard, herd) it.
5. I do (knot, not) (know, no) of a person who is (knot, not) ready to help the hungry people of the world.
6. Michelle, you (seam, seem) to have forgotten about (our, hour) plans for the picnic.
7. Who (won, one) the citizenship (medal, meddle) this year?
8. Jim, how much do you (way, weigh)?
9. The night (air, heir) is (sew, so) cool that you will (knead, need) a light jacket.
10. The small plants were set out in orderly (rows, rose).
11. I (knew, new) those (knew, new) shoes would hurt my (feat, feet).
12. Which states lead in the production of (beat, beet) sugar?
13. We did (not, knot) go to the (seen, scene) of the wreck.
14. Sue wore the belt around her (waist, waste).

B. Write a homonym for each word below.

1. peace ____________
2. altar ____________
3. to ____________
4. way ____________
5. beech ____________
6. plain ____________
7. coarse ____________
8. seem ____________
9. knew ____________
10. sale ____________
11. sew ____________
12. break ____________
13. week ____________
14. rein ____________
15. bare ____________
16. scene ____________
17. mite ____________
18. whole ____________
19. hoarse ____________
20. fourth ____________
21. knight ____________
22. hymn ____________
23. through ____________
24. grown ____________
25. wrap ____________
26. prey ____________
27. strait ____________
28. sole ____________
29. hear ____________
30. ware ____________

homework 2/15/2017

Lesson 3 Homographs

- A **homograph** is a word that has the same spelling as another word but a different meaning and sometimes a different pronunciation.
  EXAMPLE: saw, meaning "have seen," and saw, meaning "a tool used for cutting"

A. Circle the letter for the definition that best defines each underlined homograph.

1. Sara jumped at the bangs of the exploding balloons.
   a. fringe of hair (b.) loud noises
2. She grabbed a stick to arm herself against the threat.
   a. part of the body (b.) take up a weapon
3. The dog's bark woke the family.
   (a.) noise a dog makes b. outside covering on a tree
4. Mix the pancake batter for three minutes.
   a. person at bat (b.) mixture for cooking

B. Use the homographs in the box to complete the sentences below. Each homograph will be used twice.

duck
alight
can
checkers

1. Pieces of a board game are checkers.
   People who are cashiers are checkers.
2. A water bird is a duck.
   To lower the head is to duck.
3. A metal container is a can.
   If you are able, you can.
4. To get down from something is to a light.
   If something is on fire, it is alight.

C. Write the homograph for each pair of meanings below. The first letter of each word is given for you.

1. a. place for horses b. delay s stall
2. a. a metal fastener b. a sound made with fingers s snap
3. a. to crush b. a yellow vegetable s squash
4. a. a bad doctor b. the sound made by a duck q quack
5. a. to strike b. a party fruit drink p punch

end

homework 2/15/2017

Lesson 4 Prefixes

■ A **prefix** added to the beginning of a base word changes the meaning of the word.

EXAMPLE: dis-, meaning "opposite of," + the base word appear = disappear, meaning "the opposite of appear"

EXAMPLES:

prefix	meaning	prefix	meaning
in-	not	re-	again
dis-	not	fore-	before
un-	not	pre-	before
trans-	across	mis-	wrong
		with-	from, against

■ **Write a new word using one of the prefixes listed above. Then write the meaning of the new word.**

WORD	NEW WORD	MEANING
1. fair	unfair	not fair to someone.
2. justice	injustice	not being served proper justice.
3. tell	foretell	telling the future.
4. warn	forewarn	warned you before.
5. visible	invisible	not being able to be seen.
6. spell	misspell	to spell incorrectly.
7. agree	disagree	not agreeing with someone.
8. see	foresee	to see before it happens.
9. behave	misbehave	not acting according to rules.
10. stand	withstand	stand aginst something.
11. complete	incomplete	not finishing something.
12. please	displease	unhappy.
13. drawn	withdrawn	to take something out.
14. likely	unlikely	not going to happen.
15. match	mismatch	not the same.
16. clean	unclean	dirty.
17. understand	misunderstand	not getting a subject.
18. correct	incorrect	not right.

Start

homework 2/15/2017

Lesson 5 Suffixes

- A **suffix** added to the end of a base word changes the meaning of the word.
  EXAMPLE: -less, meaning "without," + the base word worth = worthless, meaning "without worth"

  EXAMPLES:

suffix	meaning	suffix	meaning
-less	without	-ist	one skilled in
-ish	of the nature of	-tion	art of
-ous	full of	-ful	full of
-en	to make	-al	pertaining to
-hood	state of being	-able	able to be
-ward	in the direction of	-ible	able to be
-ness	quality of		

- Sometimes you need to change the spelling of a base word when a suffix is added.
  EXAMPLE: happy – happiness

- **Write a new word using one of the suffixes listed above. Then write the meaning of the new word.**

WORD	NEW WORD	MEANING
1. care	careless	not careful.
2. truth	thuthful	doesn't lie.
3. fame	famous	some one popular.
4. soft	softness	a very nice texture.
5. down	downward	direction going down.
6. light	lighten	object that can light up.
7. east	eastward	going in that direction.
8. honor	honorable	worthy of honor.
9. thank	thankfull	full of thank.
10. rest	restful	soothing quality.
11. child	childish	being a child.
12. remark	remarkable	worthy of attetion.
13. violin	violinist	someone that plays violin.
14. courage	courageous	to be brave.
15. worth	worthless	having no worth.

end

classwork 3/13/2017

Lesson 6 Contractions

- A **contraction** is a word formed by joining two other words.
- An **apostrophe** shows where a letter or letters have been omitted.
  EXAMPLE: had not = hadn't
- Won't is an exception.
  EXAMPLE: will not = won't

A. Write the contraction for each pair of words.

1. did not didn't
2. was not wasn't
3. we are we're
4. is not isn't
5. who is who's
6. had not hadn't
7. I will I'll
8. I am I'm
9. it is it's
10. do not don't
11. they have They've
12. would not wouldn't
13. will not won't
14. does not doesn't
15. were not weren't
16. there is there's
17. could not couldn't
18. I have I've
19. she will She'll
20. they are They're

B. Underline each contraction. Write the words that make up the contraction on the lines.

1. They're dusting the piano very carefully before they inspect it. They are
2. They'll want to look closely, in case there are any scratches. They will
3. If it's in good condition, Mary will buy it. It is
4. Mary's an excellent piano player. Mary is
5. Her friends think she'll earn a college scholarship with her talent. She will
6. Tom doesn't play the piano, but he's a great cook. does not he is
7. He'd like to be a professional chef. He would
8. His friends would've liked for him to go to college. would have
9. But they aren't concerned as long as Tom's happy. are not Tom is
10. Tom and Mary think they've got very supportive friends. They have

classwork 3/13/2017

Lesson 7 Compound Words

- A **compound word** is a word that is made up of two or more words. The meaning of many compound words is related to the meaning of each individual word.

  EXAMPLE: blue + berry = blueberry, meaning "a type of berry that is blue in color"

- Compound words may be written as one word, as hyphenated words, or as two separate words. Always check a dictionary.

A. Combine the words in the list to make compound words. You may use words more than once.

air	knob	door	port	paper	condition	black	berry
sand	line	stand	under	way	ground	bird	sea

1. door knob
2. blachberry
3. air way
4. sand paper
5. underground
6. seaport
7. blachbird
8. air condition
9. under line
10. understand
11. underway
12. doorway

B. Answer the following questions.

1. Whirl means "to move in circles." What is a whirlpool?

   A tub where water moves \ Jacuzzi.

2. Since quick means "moves rapidly," what is quicksand?

   sinh quichley.

3. Rattle means "to make sharp, short sounds quickly." What is a rattlesnake?

   lives.

4. A ring is "a small, circular band." What is an earring?

   for ear.

5. Pool can mean "a group of people who do something together." What is a car pool?

   go together.

6. A lace can be "a string or cord that is used to hold something together." What is a shoelace?

   to tie your shoe.

classwork 5/15/2017

Lesson 8 Connotation/Denotation

- The **denotation** of a word is its exact meaning as stated in a dictionary.
  EXAMPLE: The denotation of stingy is "ungenerous" or "miserly."
- The **connotation** of a word is an added meaning that suggests something positive or negative.
  EXAMPLES: **Negative:** Stingy suggests "ungenerous." Stingy has a negative connotation.
  Positive: Economical suggests "efficient" and "careful." Economical has a positive connotation.
- Some words are neutral. They do not suggest either good or bad feelings.
  EXAMPLES: garage, kitchen, roof

A. Write (–) if the underlined word has a negative connotation. Write (+) if it has a positive connotation. Write (N) if the word is neutral.

N 1. This is my house.

\+ 2. This is my home.

N 3. Darren's friends discussed his problem.

– 4. Darren's friends gossiped about his problem.

N 5. Our dog is sick.

– 6. Our dog is diseased.

N 7. The play was enjoyable.

\+ 8. The play was fantastic.

– 9. Julie is boring.

N 10. Julie is quiet.

B. Fill each blank with the word that suggests the connotation given.

1. Our experience of the storm was horrible. (negative) 2. Our experience of the storm was exciting. (positive) 3. Our experience of the storm was unpleasant. (neutral)	unpleasant exciting horrible
4. Monica is old. (neutral) 5. Monica is mature. (positive) 6. Monica is over the hill. (negative)	old over-the-hill mature

classwork 5/15/2017

Lesson 9 Idioms

■ An **idiom** is an expression that has a meaning different from the usual meanings of the individual words within it.
EXAMPLE: Lit a fire under me means "got me going," not "burned me."

A. Underline the idiom in each sentence. Then write what the idiom means.

1. Jack and Ellen knew they were in hot water when their car died.
your in troble
2. They were miles from any town, and Ellen was beside herself.
your very upset
3. Jack said they should put their heads together and find a solution.
make a plan, share ideas
4. Ellen told Jack that if he had any ideas, she was all ears.
i'm listening
5. Jack told her it was too soon to throw in the towel.
to give up

B. Underline each idiom. Then write one definition that tells the exact meaning of the phrase and another definition that tells what the phrase means in the sentence.

1. When I finish the test, I'm going to hit the road.
   a. Pound on the street
   b. Leave
2. I had to eat crow when I found out I was wrong about the test date.
   a. to eat a bird.
   b. apologize/admit your mistake.
3. With final exams coming, I'll have to burn the midnight oil.
   a. to burn oil.
   b. stay up late.
4. I thought I was so smart, but that test really cut me down to size.
   a. cut someone.
   b. taught a lesson, reality check.

classwork 5/15/2017

Review

A. Write S before each pair of synonyms. Write A before each pair of antonyms.

A **1.** quiet, noisy
S **2.** fearless, brave
S **3.** begin, start
A **4.** gentle, rough
A **5.** healthy, sick
S **6.** calm, peaceful
A **7.** lost, found
A **8.** night, day
S **9.** fast, quick
S **10.** cry, weep
A **11.** bottom, top
A **12.** dull, sharp

B. Using the homonyms in parentheses, write the correct words on the lines.

1. (week, weak) Anna was weak for a week after she had the flu.

2. (right, write) Did you write down the right address?

3. (blew, blue) The wind blew leaves and twigs into the beautiful blue water.

4. (read, red) Meg read a poem about a young girl with red hair and freckles.

5. (pane, pain) Maria felt a pain in her hand when she tried to remove the broken window pane.

C. Circle the letter of the best definition for each underlined homograph.

1. John flies to California every summer to visit his family.
a. insects **b.** moves in the air

2. Mr. Bailey owns a fruit and vegetable stand.
a. to be on one's feet **b.** a small, open structure

3. The band enjoyed performing at the ball.
a. a large formal dance **b.** a round body or object

4. Don't forget to wind the alarm clock before you go to bed.
a. air movement **b.** to tighten a spring

D. Choose an appropriate prefix or suffix from the box for each of the underlined words below. Write the new word on the line.

dis-	mis-	re-	un-	-ish	-ful	-less	-en

1. full of thanks thankful
2. to pay again repay
3. to not agree disagree
4. act as a fool foolish
5. to make black in color blacken
6. without thanks thankless
7. not happy unhappy
8. take wrongly mistake

E. Underline the pair of words that can be written as a contraction in each sentence. Then write each contraction on the line.

_______ 1. Yolanda does not want to work late today.

_______ 2. She would rather come in early tomorrow.

_______ 3. It is getting dark.

_______ 4. She does not like driving in the dark.

_______ 5. You must not blame her.

_______ 6. Who is going to stay with her?

_______ 7. James did not volunteer.

F. Combine two words in each sentence to make a compound word. Write the word on the line.

1. I polished the brass knob on the door. _______
2. Lynn rested her swollen foot on the stool. _______
3. The police tried to block the road to catch the thief. _______
4. Please walk on the left side of the street. _______
5. I keep my green plants in my warm house during the winter. _______

G. Write (–) if the underlined word has a negative connotation. Write (+) if the underlined word has a positive connotation.

_______ 1. Joe is sometimes narrow-minded.

_______ 2. Marie is very outgoing.

_______ 3. Do you like to gossip?

_______ 4. Carla can gab for hours.

_______ 5. Let's donate this later.

_______ 6. The child grabbed the toy and ran away.

_______ 7. Those insects are real pests.

_______ 8. I demand that you listen to me.

_______ 9. The mansion was very old.

_______ 10. Steve drives an old jalopy.

H. Underline the idiom in each sentence. Then write what the idiom means.

1. Since there was little time, the mayor only hit the high spots of his speech.

____

2. The committee's bank account was low, so they had to cut corners on their party.

____

3. Mark couldn't find a job, so he asked his uncle to pull some strings for him.

____

Using What You've Learned

A. On the line before each sentence, write synonym, antonym, homonym, or homograph to describe the pair of underlined words.

Synonym 1. You may give an answer, but be sure of your reply.

Homonym 2. Be very careful in your explanation of the bee.

Homograph 3. The bank on the river bank refused my request for a loan.

Homonym 4. I ate dinner at eight last night.

Synonym 5. Look in the closet to see if my protective suit is there.

Antonym 6. Randy knew the answer to the question about bee colonies.

Antonym 7. Why are you making such a big fuss over such a little thing as a bee sting?

B. In each sentence, underline the word that contains a prefix or a suffix. Then write a definition of that word.

1. Jiro was thankful for a chance to play.
   full of thanks.
2. Connie was very unhappy about missing the ball.
   not happy.
3. The coach was displeased at our performance.
   not pleased.
4. It was a thankless job, but someone had to clean up the park.
   without thanks.
5. We repainted the bleachers this summer.
   painted again.
6. We will transplant flower bulbs this fall.
7. We were unsure that it would be done by Saturday.
   not sure

C. Write the words that make up each contraction below.

1. won't will not
2. I'm I am
3. it's it is
4. weren't were not
5. she'll She will
6. we're we are

D. Write (–) if the definition has a negative connotation. Write (N) if the definition is neutral.

1. **desert**	N	leave	–	abandon
2. **curious**	–	nosy; prying	N	eager to know
3. **clown**	N	circus performer	–	silly actor
4. **jungle**	–	hectic, crowded place	N	place with much plant growth
5. **anxious**	N	concerned	–	nervous; full of fear
6. **fall**	N	drop	–	plunge
7. **look**	N	view	–	stare; gawk
8. **response**	–	excuse	N	explanation

E. Rewrite the paragraph. Replace the idioms with other words or phrases that have the same meaning as the idioms.

"I'd take the rumor about the test with a grain of salt," Tom said. "Our teacher knows we're on top of the world about the class party. I'm sure she wouldn't knock the pins out from under us by making us hit the books now for a test. We've been trying to find out, but she hasn't spilled the beans yet. Maybe we'd better stop beating around the bush and ask her. I'd hate to end up just taking a shot in the dark on an important test."

Lesson 10 Recognizing Sentences

■ A **sentence** is a group of words that expresses a complete thought.
EXAMPLE: We found a deserted cabin at the top of the hill.

■ **Some of the following groups of words are sentences, and some are not. Write S before each group that is a sentence. Punctuate each sentence with a period.**

_____ **1.** Tomás did not go to the auto show___

_____ **2.** By the side of the babbling brook___

_____ **3.** I went to the new museum last week___

_____ **4.** Mile after mile along the great highway___

_____ **5.** Check all work carefully___

_____ **6.** Down the narrow aisle of the church___

_____ **7.** I have lost my hat___

_____ **8.** On our way to work this morning___

_____ **9.** Leontyne Price, a famous singer___

_____ **10.** We saw Katherine and Sheryl yesterday___

_____ **11.** The severe cold of last winter___

_____ **12.** Once upon a time, long, long ago___

_____ **13.** There was a gorgeous sunset last night___

_____ **14.** He ran home___

_____ **15.** My brother and my sister___

_____ **16.** Tom and Matt did a great job___

_____ **17.** We saw a beaver in the deep ravine___

_____ **18.** The cat in our neighbor's yard___

_____ **19.** Every year at the state fair___

_____ **20.** As we came to the sharp curve in the road___

_____ **21.** Just before we were ready___

_____ **22.** I heard that you and Lorenzo have a new paper route___

_____ **23.** Longfellow is called the children's poet___

_____ **24.** Into the parking garage___

_____ **25.** We washed and waxed the truck___

_____ **26.** Through the door and up the stairs___

_____ **27.** As quickly as possible___

_____ **28.** We saw the new killer whale at the zoo___

_____ **29.** John parked the car on the street___

_____ **30.** We had ice cream and fruit for dessert___

Lesson 11 Types of Sentences

- A **declarative sentence** makes a statement. It is followed by a period (.). EXAMPLE: Alicia is my cousin.
- An **interrogative sentence** asks a question. It is followed by a question mark (?). EXAMPLE: Where are you going?
- An **imperative sentence** expresses a command or request. It is followed by a period (.). EXAMPLE: Close the door.
- An **exclamatory sentence** expresses strong emotion. It can also express a command or request that is made with great excitement. It is followed by an exclamation mark (!). EXAMPLES: How you frightened me! Look at that accident!

A. Write D for declarative, IN for interrogative, IM for imperative, or E for exclamatory before each sentence. Put the correct punctuation at the end of each sentence.

_____ 1. Everyone will be here by nine o'clock___

_____ 2. Train your mind to do its work efficiently___

_____ 3. How does a canal lock work___

_____ 4. Prepare each day's assignment on time___

_____ 5. Are we going to the game now___

_____ 6. Who brought these delicious peaches___

_____ 7. Our guests have arrived___

_____ 8. What is meant by rotation of crops___

_____ 9. Please bring a glass of water___

_____ 10. Stop that noise___

_____ 11. Always stand erect___

_____ 12. Who arranged these flowers___

_____ 13. Anna, what do you have in that box___

_____ 14. The Vikings were famous sailors___

_____ 15. Have you solved all the problems in our lesson___

_____ 16. Jack, hand me that wrench___

_____ 17. What is the capital of California___

_____ 18. Cultivate a pleasant manner___

_____ 19. How is a pizza made___

_____ 20. Block that kick___

_____ 21. A nation is measured by the character of its people___

_____ 22. Are you an early riser___

_____ 23. Practice good table manners___

_______ 24. What a wonderful time we've had___

_______ 25. How did you get here so early___

_______ 26. Look out for those cars___

_______ 27. Take good care of my dog___

_______ 28. There are many cotton mills in our state___

_______ 29. Name the capital of Nevada___

_______ 30. Hurrah, the game is over___

_______ 31. Draw a map of South America___

_______ 32. Geysers were first discovered in Iceland___

_______ 33. Have you ever been on a roller coaster___

_______ 34. Sweep the front walk___

_______ 35. Do not measure people by what they have___

_______ 36. A great nation is made only by worthy citizens___

_______ 37. Anna Moffo has sung with many of the major opera companies___

_______ 38. What is the longest river in the country___

_______ 39. Oh, you have a new car___

_______ 40. Andrea, why weren't you at the meeting___

_______ 41. The organization will elect officers tomorrow___

_______ 42. Chris, I have a long piece of twine___

_______ 43. Paul, jump quickly___

B. Only one group of words in each pair below is a sentence. Circle the sentence, and tell what kind it is. Write D for declarative, IN for interrogative, IM for imperative, or E for exclamatory.

_______ 1. When will the train arrive? Two hours late.

_______ 2. It is delayed by bad weather. Not here yet.

_______ 3. From California. Juan and Shelly are on it.

_______ 4. I haven't seen them in two years! Am waiting patiently.

_______ 5. Enjoy traveling. They will stay with us for two weeks.

_______ 6. We have many things planned for them. A good visit.

_______ 7. Sleep in the guest room. To our city's new zoo?

_______ 8. Juan used to work at a zoo. Many animals.

_______ 9. Go in the reptile house. Took care of the elephants.

_______ 10. Each elephant had a name. Wally, Sandra, and Joe.

_______ 11. The elephants liked to train with Juan. Good job.

_______ 12. Sandra, the elephant, had a baby. In the zoo.

_______ 13. Male elephant. What did the zoo officials name the baby?

_______ 14. People in the zoo. They surprised Juan!

_______ 15. He never had an elephant named for him before! Seal exhibit.

Complete Subjects and Predicates

- Every sentence has two main parts, a **complete subject** and a **complete predicate.**
- The complete subject includes all the words that tell who or what the sentence is about. EXAMPLE: **All chickadees**/hunt insect eggs.
- The complete predicate includes all the words that state the action or condition of the subject. EXAMPLE: All chickadees/**hunt insect eggs.**

A. Draw a line between the complete subject and the complete predicate in each sentence below.

1. Amy/built a bird feeder for the backyard.
2. This cleaner will remove paint.
3. Many beautiful waltzes were composed by Johann Strauss.
4. Queen Victoria ruled England for many years.
5. Eighty people are waiting in line for tickets.
6. Mario's last visit was during the summer.
7. The rocket was soon in orbit.
8. Our last meeting was held in my living room.
9. The farmers are harvesting their wheat.
10. Our new house has six rooms.
11. The heart pumps blood throughout the body.
12. This computer will help you work faster.
13. My friend has moved to Santa Fe, New Mexico.
14. A deep silence fell upon the crowd.
15. The police officers were stopping the speeding motorists.
16. The French chef prepared excellent food.
17. My father is a mechanic.
18. José Salazar is running for the city council.
19. Lightning struck a tree in our yard.
20. Magazines about bicycling are becoming increasingly popular.
21. They answered every question honestly during the interview.
22. The gray twilight came before the program ended.
23. Steve has a way with words.
24. That section of the country has many pine forests.
25. We will have a party for Teresa on Friday.
26. Butterflies flew around the flowers.
27. The heavy bus was stuck in the mud.

B. Write a sentence by adding a complete predicate to each complete subject.

1. All of the students ______________________________
2. Elephants ______________________________
3. The top of the mountain ______________________________
4. The television programs tonight ______________________________
5. I ______________________________
6. Each of the girls ______________________________
7. My father's truck ______________________________
8. The dam across the river ______________________________
9. Our new station wagon ______________________________
10. You ______________________________
11. The books in our bookcase ______________________________
12. The mountains ______________________________
13. Today's paper ______________________________
14. The magazine staff ______________________________

C. Write a sentence by adding a complete subject to each complete predicate.

1. ______________________________ is the largest city in Mexico.
2. ______________________________ came to our program.
3. ______________________________ is a valuable mineral.
4. ______________________________ grow beside the road.
5. ______________________________ traveled day and night.
6. ______________________________ was a great inventor.
7. ______________________________ wrote the letter of complaint.
8. ______________________________ met us at the airport.
9. ______________________________ made ice cream for the picnic.
10. ______________________________ made a nest in our tree.
11. ______________________________ lives near the shopping center.
12. ______________________________ have a meeting on Saturday.

Simple Subjects and Predicates

- The **simple subject** of a sentence is the main word in the complete subject. The simple subject is a noun or a pronoun. Sometimes the simple subject is also the complete subject. EXAMPLES: Our **car**/swayed in the strong wind. **Cars**/sway in the strong wind.

A. Draw a line between the complete subject and the complete predicate in each sentence below. Then underline the simple subject.

1. The plants sprouted quickly after the first rain.
2. The television program was very informative.
3. I used a word processor to write the paper.
4. My friend's truck is parked in the driveway.
5. The beavers created a dam in the river.
6. The books lined the shelves like toy soldiers.
7. Hail pounded against the storm door.
8. I bought a new mountain bike.
9. My favorite subject is history.
10. The colorful bird sang a beautiful melody.
11. The tree trunk was about five feet in diameter.
12. The sidewalk had cracks in the pavement.

- The **simple predicate** of a sentence is a verb within the complete predicate. The simple predicate may be made up of one word or more than one word. EXAMPLES: Our car/**swayed.** The wind/**was blowing** hard.

B. In each sentence below, draw a line between the complete subject and the complete predicate. Underline the simple predicate twice.

1. A rare Chinese vase was on display.
2. Many of the children had played.
3. All of the group went on a hike.
4. He drove the bus slowly over the slippery pavement.
5. A large number of water-skiers were on the lake last Saturday.
6. Birds have good eyesight.
7. Who discovered the Pacific Ocean?
8. I am reading the assignment now.
9. The glare of the headlights blinded us.
10. The problem on the next page is harder.

Lesson 14

Position of Subjects

- When the subject of a sentence comes before the verb, the sentence is in **natural order.** EXAMPLE: Maria went home.
- When the verb or part of the verb comes before the subject, the sentence is in **inverted order.** EXAMPLES: On the branch were two birds.
  There are four children in my family. Here is my friend.
- Many questions are in inverted order. EXAMPLE: Where is Jim?
- Sometimes the subject of a sentence is not expressed, as in a command or request. The understood subject is you. EXAMPLES: Bring the sandwiches. (You) bring the sandwiches.

- **Rewrite each inverted sentence in natural order. Rewrite commands or requests by including you as the subject. Then underline each simple subject once and each simple predicate twice in each sentence you write.**

1. Where was the sunken treasure ship?
   The sunken treasure ship was where?
2. Beyond the bridge were several sailboats.
3. There is no one in that room.
4. From the gymnasium came the shouts of the victorious team.
5. Beside the walk grew beautiful flowers.
6. When is the surprise party?
7. Bring your sales report to the meeting.
8. There were only three floats in the parade.
9. From the yard came the bark of a dog.
10. Place the forks to the left of the plate.

Lesson 15 Compound Subjects

- A **compound subject** is made up of two or more simple subjects.
  EXAMPLE: **Henri** and **Tanya** / are tall people.

A. Draw a line between the complete subject and the complete predicate in each sentence. Write SS for a simple subject. Write CS for a compound subject.

CS 1. Arturo and I/often work late on Friday.
_____ 2. Sandy left the person near the crowded exit.
_____ 3. She and I will mail the packages to San Francisco, California, today.
_____ 4. Shanghai and New Delhi are two cities visited by the group.
_____ 5. The fire spread rapidly to other buildings in the neighborhood.
_____ 6. Luis and Lenora helped their parents with the chores.
_____ 7. Swimming, jogging, and hiking were our favorite sports.
_____ 8. Melbourne and Sydney are important Australian cities.
_____ 9. Eric and I had an interesting experience Saturday.
_____ 10. The Red Sea and the Mediterranean Sea are connected by the Suez Canal.
_____ 11. The Republicans and the Democrats made many speeches before the election.
_____ 12. The people waved to us from the top of the cliff.
_____ 13. Liz and Jim crated the freshly-picked apples.
_____ 14. Clean clothes and a neat appearance are important in an interview.
_____ 15. The kitten and the old dog are good friends.
_____ 16. David and Paul are on their way to the swimming pool.
_____ 17. Tom combed his dog's shiny black coat.
_____ 18. Redbud and dogwood trees bloom in the spring.
_____ 19. I hummed a cheerful tune on the way to the meeting.
_____ 20. Buffalo, deer, and antelope once roamed the plains of North America.
_____ 21. Gina and Hiroshi raked the leaves.
_____ 22. Brasília and São Paulo are two cities in Brazil.
_____ 23. Hang gliding is a popular sport in Hawaii.
_____ 24. Our class went on a field trip to the aquarium.
_____ 25. The doctor asked him to get a blood test.

B. Write two sentences containing compound subjects.

1. ______________________________

2. ______________________________

Lesson 16 Compound Predicates

■ A **compound predicate** is made up of two or more simple predicates.
EXAMPLE: Joseph / **dances** and **sings.**

A. Draw a line between the complete subject and the complete predicate in each sentence. Write SP for each simple predicate. Write CP for each compound predicate.

CP 1. Edward / grinned and nodded.
_____ 2. Plants need air to live.
_____ 3. Old silver tea kettles were among their possessions.
_____ 4. My sister buys and sells real estate.
_____ 5. Snow covered every highway in the area.
_____ 6. Mr. Sanders designs and makes odd pieces of furniture.
_____ 7. Popcorn is one of my favorite snack foods.
_____ 8. Soccer is one of my favorite sports.
_____ 9. The ducks quickly crossed the road and found the ducklings.
_____ 10. They came early and stayed late.
_____ 11. Crystal participated in the Special Olympics this year.
_____ 12. José raked and sacked the leaves.
_____ 13. Perry built the fire and cooked supper.
_____ 14. We collected old newspapers for the recycling center.
_____ 15. Doug arrived in Toronto, Ontario, during the afternoon.
_____ 16. Tony's parents are visiting in Oregon and Washington.
_____ 17. The Garzas live in that apartment building on Oak Street.
_____ 18. The shingles were picked up and delivered today.
_____ 19. The audience talked and laughed before the performance.
_____ 20. Automobiles crowd and jam that highway early in the morning.
_____ 21. The apples are rotting in the boxes.
_____ 22. The leader of the group grumbled and scolded.
_____ 23. She worked hard and waited patiently.
_____ 24. Nelson Mandela is a great civil rights activist.
_____ 25. The supervisor has completed the work for the week.

B. Write two sentences containing compound predicates.

1. ____

2. ____

Lesson 17 Combining Sentences

- Two sentences in which the subjects are different and the predicates are the same can be combined into one sentence. The two subjects are joined by and. EXAMPLE: **Hurricanes** are storms. **Tornadoes** are storms. **Hurricanes and tornadoes** are storms.
- Two sentences in which the subjects are the same and the predicates are different can be combined into one sentence. The two predicates may be joined by or, and, or but. EXAMPLE: Hurricanes **begin over tropical oceans.** Hurricanes **move inland.** Hurricanes **begin over tropical oceans and move inland.**

- **Combine each pair of sentences below. Underline the compound subject or the compound predicate in each sentence that you write.**

1. Lightning is part of a thunderstorm. Thunder is part of a thunderstorm.

 ____

2. Thunderstorms usually happen in the spring. Thunderstorms bring heavy rains.

 ____

3. Depending on how close or far away it is, thunder sounds like a sharp crack. Depending on how close or far away it is, thunder rumbles.

 ____

 ____

4. Lightning is very exciting to watch. Lightning can be very dangerous.

 ____

5. Lightning causes many fires. Lightning harms many people.

 ____

6. An open field is an unsafe place to be during a thunderstorm. A golf course is an unsafe place to be during a thunderstorm.

 ____

 ____

7. Benjamin Franklin wanted to protect people from lightning. Benjamin Franklin invented the lightning rod.

 ____

 ____

8. A lightning rod is a metal rod placed on the top of a building. A lightning rod is connected to the ground by a cable.

 ____

 ____

Lesson 18 Direct Objects

- The **direct object** tells who or what receives the action of the verb. The direct object is a noun or pronoun that follows an action verb.

  EXAMPLE: You told the **truth.** (DO)

- **Underline the verb in each sentence. Then write DO above each direct object.**

1. Elephants can carry logs with their trunks. (DO: logs; verb: can carry)
2. Who made this magazine rack?
3. Do you always plan a daily schedule?
4. They easily won the game.
5. Martin baked an apple pie for dinner.
6. Who tuned your piano?
7. I take guitar lessons once a week.
8. Who composed this melody?
9. I especially enjoy mystery stories.
10. The astronauts orbited the earth many times.
11. I bought this coat in New York.
12. Did he find his glasses?
13. Anne drove the truck to the hardware store.
14. The boy shrugged his shoulders.
15. We have finished our work today.
16. We drink milk with breakfast.
17. She can solve any problem quickly.
18. Who made our first flag?
19. You will learn something from this lesson.
20. Every person needs friends.
21. I have found a dime.
22. Yuko ate an apple for a snack.

Indirect Objects

- The **indirect object** is the noun or pronoun that tells to whom or for whom an action is done. In order to have an indirect object, a sentence must have a direct object.
- The indirect object is usually placed between the action verb and the direct object.

  EXAMPLE: Who sold **you** (IO) that fantastic **bike?** (DO)

- **Underline the verb in each sentence. Then write DO above the direct object and IO above the indirect object.**

1. Certain marine plants give the Red Sea (IO) its color (DO).
2. I gave the cashier a check for twenty dollars.
3. The magician showed the audience a few of her tricks.
4. The coach taught them the rules of the game.
5. Roberto brought us some foreign coins.
6. This interesting book will give every reader pleasure.
7. Have you written your brother a letter?
8. They made us some sandwiches to take on our hike.
9. The astronaut gave Mission Control the data.
10. I bought my friend an etching at the art exhibit.
11. James, did you sell Mike your car?
12. We have given the dog a thorough scrubbing.
13. Give the usher your ticket.
14. Carl brought my brother a gold ring from Mexico.
15. Hand me a pencil, please.
16. The conductor gave the orchestra a short break.
17. Show me the picture of your boat.
18. I have given you my money.
19. Give Lee this message.
20. The club gave the town a new statue.

Lesson 20 Independent and Subordinate Clauses

- A **clause** is a group of words that contains a subject and a predicate. There are two kinds of clauses: **independent clauses** and **subordinate clauses.**
- An **independent clause** can stand alone as a sentence because it expresses a complete thought.
  EXAMPLE: **The students came in** when the bell rang. **The students came in.**

A. Underline the independent clause in each sentence below.

1. Frank will be busy because he is studying.
2. I have only one hour that I can spare.
3. The project must be finished when I get back.
4. Gloria volunteered to do the typing that needs to be done.
5. The work is going too slowly for us to finish on time.
6. Before Nathan started to help, I didn't think we could finish.
7. What else should we do before we relax?
8. Since you forgot to give this page to Gloria, you can type it.
9. After she had finished typing, we completed the project.
10. We actually got it finished before the deadline.

- A **subordinate clause** has a subject and predicate but cannot stand alone as a sentence because it does not express a complete thought. A subordinate clause must be combined with an independent clause to make a sentence.
  EXAMPLE: The stamp **that I bought** was already in my collection.

B. Underline the subordinate clause in each sentence below.

1. The people who went shopping found a great sale.
2. Tony's bike, which is a mountain bike, came from that store.
3. Juana was sad when the sale was over.
4. Marianne was excited because she wanted some new things.
5. Thomas didn't find anything since he went late.
6. The mall where we went shopping was new.
7. The people who own the stores are proud of the beautiful setting.
8. The mall, which is miles away, is serviced by the city bus.
9. We ran as fast as we could because the bus was coming.
10. We were panting because we had run fast.

Lesson 21 Adjective Clauses

- An **adjective clause** is a subordinate clause that modifies a noun or a pronoun. It answers the adjective question Which one? or What kind? It usually modifies the word directly preceding it. Most adjective clauses begin with a **relative pronoun.** A relative pronoun relates an adjective clause to the noun or pronoun that the clause modifies. Who, whose, which, and that are relative pronouns.

  EXAMPLE: The coat **that I bought** was on sale.
  noun adjective clause

A. Underline the adjective clause in each sentence below.

1. A compass has a needle that always points northward.
2. A seismograph is an instrument that measures earthquake tremors.
3. People who work in science laboratories today have a broad field of study.
4. This will be the first time that she has played in that position.
5. Jay is the person whose wrist was broken.
6. The fish that I caught was large.
7. A sentence that contains a subordinate clause is a complex sentence.
8. Here is the photograph that I promised to show you.
9. The book that I read was very humorous.

B. Add an adjective clause to each independent clause below.

1. A microscope is an instrument (that) ______________________________

____

2. Amelia Earhart was a pilot (who) ______________________________

____

3. We have football players (who) ______________________________

____

4. They built a helicopter (which) ______________________________

____

5. Bunny is a dog (that) ______________________________

____

6. A telescope is an instrument (that) ______________________________

____

Lesson 22 Adverb Clauses

■ An **adverb clause** is a subordinate clause that modifies a verb, an adjective, or another adverb. It answers the adverb question How? Under what condition? or Why? Words that introduce adverb clauses are called **subordinating conjunctions.** The many subordinating conjunctions include such words as when, after, before, since, although, and because. EXAMPLE: I finished **before the bell rang.** (adverb clause)

A. Underline the adverb clause in each sentence below.

1. We had agreed to go hiking when the cloudy skies cleared.
2. Although the weather was mild and sunny, we took along our jackets.
3. Clouds began to move in once again after we arrived at the park.
4. We felt comfortable about the weather because we were prepared.
5. Since we had our jackets, we didn't get too cold.
6. Although the clouds remained, it never rained.
7. It was exhilarating to see the view when we got to the top of the hill.
8. After enjoying the beauty and the quiet for a while, we hiked back down.
9. We decided to drive home the long way since it was still early.
10. We had a wonderful day because we were so relaxed and happy.

B. Add an adverb clause to each independent clause below.

1. We ate breakfast (before) ____________________

____

2. Jay and I carried umbrellas (since) ____________________

____

3. We took the bus to the museum (because) ____________________

____

4. People in line waited (when) ____________________

____

5. We saw the exhibit (after) ____________________

____

6. Joel and I baked cookies (when) ____________________

____

Lesson 23 Simple and Compound Sentences

- A **simple sentence** contains only one independent clause. The subject, the predicate, or both may be compound.
  EXAMPLES: The courthouse/is the oldest building in town. Gale and Louise/are making costumes and dressing up.
- A **compound sentence** consists of two or more independent clauses. Each independent clause in a compound sentence can stand alone as a separate sentence. The independent clauses are usually joined by and, but, so, or, for, or yet and a comma.
  EXAMPLE: Jack brought the chairs, but Mary forgot the extra table.
- Sometimes a **semicolon (;)** is used to join two independent clauses in a compound sentence.
  EXAMPLE: The music started; the dance had begun.

A. Write S before each simple sentence, and write CS before each compound sentence.

_______ **1.** We can wait for James, or we can go on ahead.

_______ **2.** The carnival will start today in the empty lot.

_______ **3.** Jack and Manuel are going to meet us there at six o'clock.

_______ **4.** I really want to go to the carnival, yet I am not sure about going tonight.

_______ **5.** I didn't mean to hurt Carl's feelings by not going.

_______ **6.** You wait for the package, and I'll meet you at the carnival.

_______ **7.** I can't skip my homework to go, but maybe I'll finish it this afternoon.

_______ **8.** Jan and Alicia are both working at the carnival this year.

B. Put brackets ([ ]) around the independent clauses in each compound sentence. Then underline the word or punctuation used to join the clauses.

1. You must observe all the rules, or you must withdraw from the race.

2. I did well on the test, and Maria did well, too.

3. Shall I carry this box, or do you want to leave it here?

4. We must closely guard our freedom, or an enemy will take it from us.

5. He threw a beautiful pass, but no one caught it.

6. The doctor treated the cut, but he did not have to make any stitches.

7. I like to spend weekends at home, but the others prefer to travel.

8. The year is almost over, and everyone is thinking of the new year.

9. The family faced every hardship, yet they were thankful for what they had.

10. Move the box over here; I'll unpack it.

11. Connie likes football; James prefers hockey.

12. I drive safely, but I always make everyone fasten seat belts.

13. Please get the telephone number, and I'll call after work.

Lesson 24 Complex Sentences

- A **complex sentence** contains one independent clause and one or more subordinate clauses.

  EXAMPLE: The person **who helps me carry these** gets some dessert.
  (subordinate clause)

A. Put brackets ([ ]) around the subordinate clause, and underline the independent clause in each complex sentence below.

1. The shadows [that had fallen between the trees] were a deep purple.
2. The soldiers waded across the stream where the water was shallow.
3. They waited for me until the last bus came.
4. The fans of that team were sad when the team lost the game.
5. When George was here, he was charmed by the beauty of the hills.
6. Sophia will call for you when she is ready.
7. Some spiders that are found in Sumatra have legs seventeen inches long.
8. Those who are going will arrive on time.
9. Do not throw the bat after you've hit the ball.
10. Tell us about the trip that you made a year ago.

B. Add a subordinate clause that begins with the word in parentheses to make a complex sentence.

1. I try not to drive (where) ______________________________

____

2. The electric light is an important invention (that) ______________________________

____

3. The telephone stopped ringing (before) ______________________________

____

4. He is the man (who) ______________________________

____

5. This is the book (that) ______________________________

____

6. Turn to the left (when) ______________________________

____

Lesson 25 Correcting Run-on Sentences

- Two or more independent clauses that are run together without the correct punctuation are called a **run-on sentence.**
  EXAMPLE: The music was deafening I turned down the volume.
- One way to correct a run-on sentence is to separate it into two sentences.
  EXAMPLE: The music was deafening. I turned down the volume.
- Another way to correct a run-on sentence is to make it into a compound sentence.
  EXAMPLE: The music was deafening, so I turned down the volume.
- Another way to correct a run-on sentence is to use a semicolon.
  EXAMPLE: The music was deafening; I turned down the volume.

- **Correct each run-on sentence below by writing it as two sentences or as a compound sentence.**

1. The city council held a meeting a meeting is held every month.

____

____

2. The council members are elected by the voters there are two thousand voters in the city.

____

____

3. There is one council member from each suburb, the president is elected by the council members.

____

____

4. Those who run for office must give speeches, the speeches should be short.

____

____

5. The council decides on many activities every activity is voted on.

____

____

6. Money is needed for many of the special activities, the council also plans fund-raisers in the city.

____

____

7. The annual city picnic is sponsored by the city council the picnic is in May.

____

____

Lesson 26 Expanding Sentences

- Sentences can be **expanded** by adding details to make them clearer and more interesting. EXAMPLE: The audience laughed. The **excited** audience **in the theater** laughed **loudly.**
- Details added to sentences may answer these questions: When? Where? How? How often? To what degree? What kind? Which? How many?

A. Expand each sentence below by adding details to answer the questions shown in parentheses. Write the expanded sentence on the line.

1. The car stalled. (What kind? Where?)

____

2. Mary raised the hood. (How? Which?)

____

3. Smoke billowed from the engine. (What kind? Where?)

____

4. She called the service station. (When? Which?)

____

5. The phone rang. (Which? How often?)

____

B. Decide how each of the following sentences can be expanded. Write your expanded sentence on the line.

1. The runner crossed the finish line.

____

2. The crowd cheered.

____

3. The reporter interviewed her.

____

4. She answered.

____

5. Her coach ran up to her.

____

6. She and her coach walked off the track.

____

7. She was awarded the medal.

____

Review

A. Label each sentence as follows: Write D for declarative, IN for interrogative, IM for imperative, or E for exclamatory. Write X if it is not a sentence. Punctuate each sentence correctly.

_______ 1. Did you forget our appointment____

_______ 2. Be careful____

_______ 3. Rolled up our sleeping bags____

_______ 4. All members will meet in this room____

_______ 5. Help, I'm frightened____

_______ 6. Where are you going____

_______ 7. Oh, look out ____

_______ 8. People from all over the world____

_______ 9. Julie ran two miles____

_______ 10. Place the books here____

B. In each sentence below, underline the words that are identified in parentheses.

1. (complete subject) The lights around the public square went out.
2. (simple subject) Stations are in all parts of our country.
3. (direct object) Carmen collects fans for a hobby.
4. (complete predicate) We drove slowly across the bridge.
5. (simple predicate) We saw an unusual flower.
6. (compound predicate) Taro swims and dives quite well.
7. (compound subject) The cake and bread are kept in the box.
8. (indirect object) The referee gave our team a fifteen-yard penalty.
9. (direct object) A good citizen obeys the laws, but a bad citizen doesn't.
10. (indirect object) Please lend me your raincoat, so I can stay dry.

C. Write CP after each compound sentence and CX after each complex sentence.

1. The food that is needed will be bought. _______
2. Mary will get lettuce, but we may have some. _______
3. Jack, who said he would help, is late. _______
4. We will go, and they will meet us. _______
5. Jack will drive his car after it has been repaired. _______
6. We are going to Spruce Park since it is on a lake. _______
7. There are canoes that can be rented. _______
8. We can row around the lake, or we can go swimming. _______
9. We can decide what we want to do after we eat our picnic lunch. _______
10. Spruce Park is a great place, and we are going to have a wonderful time. _______

D. Underline the verb in each sentence. Then write DO above the direct object and IO above the indirect object.

1. The director gave the actors a new script.
2. Jenny showed her friends her vacation slides.
3. Ms. Lopez took her sick neighbor some chicken soup.
4. We handed the cashier our money.
5. Enrique, please give your brother his jacket.

E. Underline the independent clause, and circle the subordinate clause in each sentence.

1. The campers got wet when it started raining.
2. The candidates that I voted for in the election won easily.
3. Before the board voted on the issue, it held public hearings.
4. The freeway through town is a road where vehicles often speed.
5. While we waited, the children kept us entertained.

F. Underline the subordinate clause in each sentence. Write adjective clause or adverb clause on the line after each sentence.

1. Meteorologists are people who are trained in weather forecasting. ________________
2. Before I decided on a college, I did many hours of research. ________________
3. The experiment that I designed failed completely. ________________
4. Although the furniture was old, it was very comfortable. ________________
5. Many people exercise because they want to stay healthy. ________________
6. I ate breakfast before I left. ________________

G. Rewrite each sentence in natural order.

1. Just below the surface lay a large goldfish.

____

2. Over the roof flew the baseball.

____

H. Combine each pair of sentences to form a compound sentence.

1. Dogs are Erica's favorite animal. Cats are John's favorite animal.

____

2. The water reflected the sun. We put on our sunglasses.

____

Using What You've Learned

A. Read the sentences in the box. Then answer the questions below.

> **A.** Did I give you the tickets for the show?
> **B.** This compact disc is fantastic!
> **C.** Be at my house by seven o'clock.
> **D.** You and I can ride downtown together.
> **E.** We can stop and eat before the show.

1. _______ Which sentence has a compound subject?
2. _______ Which sentence has a compound predicate?
3. _______ Which sentence has a direct object?
4. _______ Which sentence has an indirect object?
5. _______ Which sentence is interrogative?
6. _______ Which sentences are declarative?
7. _______ Which sentence is exclamatory?
8. _______ Which sentence is imperative?
9. What is the complete subject of E? ______________________________
10. What is the simple subject of E? ______________________________
11. What is the complete predicate of C? ______________________________

B. Underline the independent clause, and circle the subordinate clause in each complex sentence below.

1. The streamers sagged after we hung them.
2. Mark knows party planning because he has many parties.
3. Everyone who wants to go to the party must bring something.
4. If everyone brings something, the party will be great.
5. Unless I am wrong, the party is tomorrow.
6. As if everything had been done, Jake ran out of the room.
7. The girls who planned the party received roses.
8. I will never forget the day that I fell on my face at a party.

C. Combine each pair of sentences below to form a compound sentence.

1. The team sat in the dugout. The fans sat in the stands.

____

2. The rain finally stopped. The game continued.

____

3. It was the bottom of the ninth inning. There were two outs.

____

4. The batter swung at the pitch. The umpire called, "Strike three!"

____

D. Rewrite each inverted sentence in natural order.

1. On the rocks perched two seagulls.

____

2. Here are the supplies for the office.

____

E. Create complex sentences by adding a subordinate clause or an independent clause to each group of words below.

1. He turned down the lonely road _______________
2. When night came, _______________
3. This was the site _______________
4. After he looked around, _______________
5. He continued to drive _______________
6. When he got to the inn, _______________

F. Rewrite the paragraph below, correcting the run-on sentences.

Patricia didn't know what to do, she had a terrible problem and she was trying to solve it. No matter how hard she thought about it no answers seemed to come. She decided to take a break and not think about it for a while. She went to the mall where she always enjoyed browsing in the bookstore she wasn't even thinking about the problem, the answer just popped into her head she was so excited about solving her problem she completely forgot about the bookstore.

____

____

____

____

____

____

____

G. Read the two sentences below. Then expand each sentence by adding details to make the sentences clearer and more interesting.

The tree crashed. Everyone screamed.

____

____

Lesson 27 Nouns

- A **noun** is a word that names a person, place, thing, or quality.
  EXAMPLE: **Nancy Ford** is my **friend.**

- **Circle the nouns in each sentence.**

1. Lupe Garcia has worked here for years and is now a supervisor.
2. The triangular piece of land at the mouth of a river is called a delta.
3. Gilbert Stuart, an American artist, painted the portraits of five American presidents.
4. Albert Einstein, the greatest scientist of the 20th century, was born in Germany.
5. The greatest library of the ancient world was in Alexandria, Egypt.
6. Jim Thorpe, born in Oklahoma, is ranked among the greatest athletes in the world.
7. Mahalia Jackson was noted as a singer of spirituals.
8. Marconi invented the wireless telegraph.
9. Do you watch the parades and football games on television on New Year's Day?
10. Terry Fox, a runner who lost a leg to cancer, ran 3,339 miles across Canada.
11. The *Boston News-Letter* was the first newspaper in the United States.
12. The first wireless message was sent across the English Channel in the nineteenth century.
13. Chicago is a city on Lake Michigan.
14. His seat is by the window.
15. Kuang likes his new house.
16. They have promised their children a trip to Carlsbad Caverns.
17. Washington, D.C., is the capital of the United States.
18. France grows more food than any other country in Western Europe.
19. Maria was excited about her new car.
20. Hailstones are frozen raindrops, but snowflakes are not.
21. The days are usually warm in the summer.
22. Many rivers were named by explorers.
23. Jeff built a carport to store his boat.
24. California is home to many movie stars.
25. William Caxton printed the first book in England.
26. Chris bought tomatoes, lettuce, and cherries at the market.
27. That building has offices, stores, and apartments.
28. Leticia drove to Peoria, Illinois, to see her friend.
29. The airport was closed for five hours due to a snowstorm.
30. My pen is almost out of ink.

Common and Proper Nouns

- There are two main classes of nouns: **common nouns** and **proper nouns.**
- A **common noun** names any one of a class of objects.
  EXAMPLES: child, tree, home
- A **proper noun** names a particular person, place, or thing. It begins with a capital letter.
  EXAMPLES: Andrew Jackson, Chicago, Statue of Liberty

A. Underline the common nouns, and circle the proper nouns in each sentence.

1. In the story, a prince and a pauper changed clothing.
2. New York and Los Angeles are the largest cities in the United States.
3. Do you remember the story about Scrooge and Tiny Tim?
4. Sumatra is a large island in the Indian Ocean.
5. In the United States, hail causes more damage than tornadoes.
6. We learned to make paper from the Chinese.
7. "Rikki-tikki-tavi," by Rudyard Kipling, is a story about a mongoose.
8. *Shamrock* is the name commonly given to the national emblem of Ireland.
9. The shilling is a silver coin used in England.
10. The lights of our car were reflected in the wet pavement.
11. Nathan, did you come with Sam last Tuesday?
12. The Great Sphinx is the most famous monument in Egypt.
13. My family visited Mexico and Canada this year.

B. Write a common noun suggested by each proper noun.

1. Panama ______
2. *Treasure Island* ______
3. Linda ______
4. Kansas ______
5. Beethoven ______
6. Pacific ______
7. Iceland ______
8. Saturn ______
9. Ms. Taylor ______
10. Africa ______
11. Edison ______
12. North America ______
13. December ______
14. Toronto ______
15. University of Ottawa ______
16. Rocky Mountains ______
17. Dr. Dean ______
18. Huron ______
19. Tuesday ______
20. Thanksgiving ______

C. **Write a proper noun suggested by each common noun.**

1. continent ____________
2. mountain ____________
3. hotel ____________
4. hero ____________
5. inventor ____________
6. building ____________
7. day ____________
8. physician ____________
9. holiday ____________
10. state ____________
11. actor ____________
12. magazine ____________
13. month ____________
14. lake ____________
15. school ____________
16. river ____________
17. song ____________
18. president ____________
19. explorer ____________
20. basketball team ____________

D. **Write a sentence in which you use a proper noun suggested to you by each phrase.**

1. Your state or province ____________
2. Name of a foreign country ____________
3. Name of a singer ____________
4. Name of the make of an automobile ____________
5. Name of a store near your home ____________
6. Name of a television star ____________
7. Name of an ocean ____________
8. Name of the President of the United States ____________

Lesson 29 Singular and Plural Nouns

The following chart shows how to change **singular nouns** into **plural nouns.**

Noun	Plural Form	Examples
Most nouns	Add -s	ship, ships nose, noses
Nouns ending in a consonant and -y	Change the -y to -i, and add -es	sky, skies navy, navies
Nouns ending in -o	Add -s or -es	hero, heroes piano, pianos
Most nouns ending in -f or -fe	Change the -f or -fe to -ves	half, halves
Most nouns ending in -ch, -sh, -s, or -x	Add -es	bench, benches bush, bushes tax, taxes
Many two-word or three-word compound nouns	Add -s to the principle word	son-in-law, sons-in-law
Nouns with the same form in the singular and plural	No change	sheep

A. Fill in the blank with the plural form of the word in parentheses.

1. (brush) These are plastic ______________________.
2. (lunch) That cafe on the corner serves well-balanced ______________________.
3. (country) What ______________________ belong to the United Nations?
4. (bench) There are many iron ______________________ in the park.
5. (earring) These ______________________ came from Italy.
6. (calf) How many ______________________ are in that pen?
7. (piano) There are three ______________________ in the warehouse.
8. (fox) Did you see the ______________________ at the zoo?
9. (daisy) We bought Susan a bunch of ______________________.
10. (potato) Do you like baked ______________________?
11. (dish) Please help wash the ______________________.
12. (store) There are three ______________________ near my house.

B. Write the correct plural form for each singular noun.

1. booklet ____________
2. tomato ____________
3. truck ____________
4. chef ____________
5. branch ____________
6. toddler ____________
7. penny ____________
8. potato ____________
9. piece ____________
10. door ____________
11. island ____________
12. country ____________
13. house ____________
14. garage ____________
15. fish ____________
16. watch ____________
17. elf ____________
18. desk ____________
19. pan ____________
20. sheep ____________
21. garden ____________
22. pony ____________
23. solo ____________
24. tree ____________
25. light ____________
26. church ____________
27. city ____________
28. spoonful ____________
29. vacation ____________
30. home ____________

C. Rewrite the sentences, changing each underlined singular noun to a plural noun.

1. Put the apple and orange in the box.

____

2. Jan wrote five letter to her friend.

____

3. Those building each have four elevator.

____

4. Our family drove many mile to get to the lake.

____

5. The top of those car were damaged in the storm.

____

6. My aunt and uncle attended the family reunion.

____

Lesson 30 Possessive Nouns

- A **possessive noun** shows possession of the noun that follows.
- Form the possessive of most singular nouns by adding an apostrophe (') and -s. EXAMPLES: a child's toy, my teacher's classroom
- Form the possessive of plural nouns ending in -s by adding only an apostrophe. EXAMPLES: our books' pages, those stores' windows
- Form the possessive of plural nouns that do not end in -s by adding an apostrophe and -s. EXAMPLES: some women's clothes, many men's shoes

A. Write the possessive form of each noun.

1. brother ______
2. boy ______
3. Carol ______
4. children ______
5. grandmother ______
6. men ______
7. heroes ______
8. women ______
9. ox ______
10. man ______
11. Dr. Kahn ______
12. soldier ______
13. pony ______
14. friend ______
15. child ______
16. engineers ______
17. birds ______
18. Jon ______

B. Write ten sentences using possessive nouns formed in Exercise A.

1. ______
2. ______
3. ______
4. ______
5. ______
6. ______
7. ______
8. ______
9. ______
10. ______

C. Complete each sentence with the possessive form of the word in parentheses.

1. (doctor) My ________________ office is closed.
2. (senator) The ________________ speech was astounding.
3. (sheep) What is the old saying about a wolf in ________________ clothing?
4. (baby) Are the ________________ hands cold?
5. (instructor) My ________________ classroom is on this floor.
6. (collectors) Let's form a ________________ club.
7. (spider) A ________________ web has a complicated design.
8. (Mr. Takata) ________________ store was damaged by the flood.
9. (Tim) ________________ brother found this purse.
10. (Beth) ________________ business is successful.
11. (Carl Sandburg) ________________ poems are enjoyed by people of all ages.
12. (child) The ________________ book is torn.
13. (women) That store sells ________________ clothing.
14. (elephants) There were seats on the ________________ backs.
15. (sister) My ________________ room is at the front of the house.
16. (Brazil) What is the name of ________________ largest river?
17. (friends) Those are my ________________ homes.
18. (bird) That ________________ nest is very close to the ground.
19. (children) The library has a table of ________________ books.
20. (owl) I heard an ________________ hoot during the night.
21. (brothers) Please get your ________________ shirts from the dryer.
22. (student) The ________________ pen ran out of ink.
23. (country) We sang our ________________ national anthem.
24. (owner) The dog lay at its ________________ feet.
25. (uncle) I visited my ________________ laundry.
26. (Joan) ________________ paintings sell well.
27. (men) The ________________ jackets are brown.

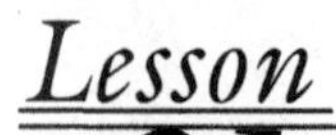

Lesson 31 Appositives

- An **appositive** is a noun that identifies or explains the noun or pronoun it follows.
  EXAMPLE: My dog, **Fido,** won a medal.
- An **appositive phrase** consists of an appositive and its modifiers.
  EXAMPLE: My book, **a novel about the Civil War,** is one of the best I've read.
- Use **commas** to set off an appositive or an appositive phrase that is not essential to the meaning of the sentence.
  EXAMPLE: John Gray, my uncle, owns that home.
- Don't use commas if the appositive is essential to the meaning of the sentence.
  EXAMPLES: My brother Kevin arrived late. My other brother Charlie arrived early.

A. Underline the appositive or appositive phrase, and circle the noun that it identifies.

1. Banff, the large Canadian national park, is my favorite place to visit.
2. The painter Vincent Van Gogh cut off part of his ear.
3. The White House, home of the President of the United States, is open to the public for tours.
4. Uncle Marco, my mother's brother, is an engineer.
5. Earth, the only inhabited planet in our solar system, is home to a diverse population of plants and animals.
6. The scorpion, a native of the southwestern part of North America, has a poisonous sting.
7. Emily's prize Persian cat Amelia won first prize at the cat show.
8. Judge Andropov, the presiding judge, sentenced the criminal to prison.
9. Paula's friend from Florida, Luisa, watched a space shuttle launch.

B. Complete each sentence with an appropriate appositive.

1. My friend ______________________ bought a new bike.
2. The bike, ______________________, is fast and sleek.
3. Joe and his friend ______________________ plan to ride their bikes together.
4. They will ride to Pease Park, ______________________, on Saturday.
5. They plan to meet Anne, ______________________, on the bike path.
6. After bicycling, they will see a movie, ______________________.
7. Our friend ______________________ might come with us.
8. We will get a snack, ______________________, to eat during the movie.
9. My favorite actor, ______________________, might be in the movie.

Action Verbs

- A **verb** is a word that expresses action, being, or state of being.
  EXAMPLE: Paul **went** to the store.
- An **action verb** is a verb that expresses action.
  EXAMPLE: The track star **ran** fast.

- **Underline the action verb in each sentence.**

1. Watch your favorite television program.
2. Andrea carefully dusted her new piano.
3. Anna, copy the pages carefully.
4. A wood fire burned in the huge fireplace.
5. This button fell from my sweater.
6. The Harlem Globe Trotters play basketball throughout the world.
7. The musicians practiced for the concert.
8. The waves dashed the light craft against the rocks.
9. A sentence expresses a complete thought.
10. Everybody enjoys a good laugh.
11. This long, narrow trail leads to the mountaintop.
12. It snowed almost every day in February.
13. We hiked through the southern part of Arizona.
14. Dan made me a delicious sandwich.
15. Please hand me the salt, Dannette.
16. Draw a line under each verb.
17. We skated on Lake Superior.
18. The woman answered all my questions.
19. The city repaired that pothole last week.
20. Early settlers suffered many hardships.
21. Write your sentence on the board.
22. They moved the car from the street.
23. Thomas Edison often worked eighteen hours a day.
24. Carol directs the community choir.
25. The team played softball all afternoon.
26. We walked along the beach for an hour.
27. Who helped you with your science project?
28. The bridge collapsed.
29. The antique clock ticked loudly.

Lesson 33 Linking Verbs

- A **linking verb** does not show action. Instead, it links the subject to a word that either describes the subject or gives the subject another name.
- A verb is a linking verb if it can replace one of the verbs of being (am, is, are, was, were).

  EXAMPLES: We **were** cold. Nancy **is** a dancer. John **looked** tired. The soup **tastes** delicious.

A. Underline the linking verb in each sentence.

1. Carla appears nervous.
2. She is the first singer on the program.
3. Last year, she was last on the program.
4. Another performer is last this year.
5. The stage looks beautiful.
6. Flowers are everywhere.
7. The flowers smell fresh.
8. Carla feels ready to start.
9. Her song sounds wonderful.
10. The audience seems pleased.

B. Complete each sentence with a linking verb from the box. You may use any verb more than once.

am	appeared	are	became	is	seemed	was	were

1. Tony ______________ frightened.
2. He ______________ alone in the cabin for the first time.
3. In the dark forest, everything ______________ threatening.
4. Because of the storm, the lights ______________ out.
5. Even the shadows ______________ strange.
6. "This ______________ stupid," he thought to himself.
7. "I ______________ brave; I'm not a coward."
8. "Where ______________ Aaron?" he wondered.
9. There ______________ bears in the woods.
10. What if he ______________ lost?

Lesson 34 Principal Parts of Verbs

- A verb has four principal parts: **present, present participle, past,** and **past participle.**
- For regular verbs, form the present participle by adding -ing to the present. Use a form of the helping verb be with the present participle.
- Form the past and past participle by adding -ed to the present. Use a form of the helping verb have with the past participle.

EXAMPLES:

Present	Present Participle	Past	Past Participle
laugh	(is) laughing	laughed	(have, has, had) laughed
bake	(is) baking	baked	(have, has, had) baked
live	(is) living	lived	(have, has, had) lived

- Irregular verbs form their past and past participle in other ways. A dictionary shows the principal parts of these verbs.

■ **Write the present participle, past, and past participle for each verb.**

PRESENT	PRESENT PARTICIPLE	PAST	PAST PARTICIPLE
1. stop	is stopping	stopped	(have, has, had) stopped
2. listen			
3. carry			
4. help			
5. start			
6. borrow			
7. call			
8. receive			
9. hope			
10. illustrate			
11. divide			
12. change			
13. score			
14. iron			
15. study			
16. collect			
17. laugh			

Lesson 35 Verb Phrases

- A **verb phrase** consists of a main verb and one or more **helping verbs.** A helping verb is also called an **auxiliary verb.** In a verb phrase, the helping verb or verbs precede the main verb. EXAMPLE: James **has arrived.**
- The helping verbs are:
  am, are, is, was, were, be, being, been
  has, have, had
  do, does, did
  can, could, must, may, might, shall, should, will, would

A. Write a sentence using each word below as the main verb in a verb phrase.

1. gone ______
2. written ______
3. come ______
4. thrown ______
5. draw ______
6. walking ______
7. invent ______
8. sing ______
9. seen ______
10. eaten ______

B. Underline the verb phrase in each sentence.

1. Isabel has returned from a vacation in Florida.
2. She has planned to tell us all about it.
3. Isabel would have answered every question about her trip.
4. Our club officers have been looking for someone to speak.
5. The officers have asked Isabel to the meeting.
6. They have organized an interesting meeting.
7. Every detail of the meeting has been planned carefully.
8. I must speak to Isabel immediately.
9. The lights were dimmed for Isabel's slide show.
10. She said that alligators had been seen in some places.
11. Pets and farm animals were threatened by them.
12. We are planning a trip to Florida next year.

Verb Tenses

- The **tense** of a verb tells the time of the action or being. There are three simple tenses—present, past, and future.
- **Present tense** tells about what is happening now.
  EXAMPLES: Conrad **is** busy. Conrad **studies** hard.
- **Past tense** tells about something that happened before.
  EXAMPLE: Conrad **was** sick yesterday.
- **Future tense** tells about something that will happen. The auxiliary verbs will and shall are used in future tense.
  EXAMPLES: Conrad **will take** the test tomorrow. I **shall keep** my word.

A. Complete each sentence by writing a verb in the tense shown in parentheses.

1. (future) Hilary ______________________ tomorrow.
2. (future) Joe ______________________ her up at the airport.
3. (past) We ______________________ the house yesterday.
4. (past) Carl ______________________ reservations for tomorrow night.
5. (present) Hilary ______________________ my friend.
6. (future) We ______________________ on a sightseeing tour.
7. (present) I ______________________ very excited about Hilary's visit.
8. (past) Margaret ______________________ Toby last week.

B. Write present, past, or future for the tense of each underlined verb.

1. Classes will end next month. ______________________
2. We studied hard yesterday. ______________________
3. Final exams will start soon. ______________________
4. I review every evening. ______________________
5. This method worked at midterm. ______________________
6. I got A's on my tests then. ______________________
7. Marty studies with me. ______________________
8. We will study every evening this week. ______________________
9. I hardly studied last year. ______________________
10. My grades showed it, too. ______________________

Present Perfect and Past Perfect Tenses

- The **perfect tenses** express action that happened before another time or event.
- The **present perfect** tense tells about something that happened at an indefinite time in the past. The present perfect tense consists of has or have + the past participle.
  EXAMPLES: I **have eaten** already. He **has eaten,** too.
- The **past perfect** tense tells about something that happened before something else in the past. The past perfect tense consists of had + the past participle.
  EXAMPLE: I already **had eaten** when they arrived.

A. Write present perfect and past perfect for the tense of the underlined verbs.

_______________ **1.** Mei had completed high school in June.

_______________ **2.** She had gone to college in Memphis before coming here.

_______________ **3.** Mei has decided that she likes her new college.

_______________ **4.** She had been worried that she wouldn't fit in.

_______________ **5.** Mei has lived in her house for eight months.

_______________ **6.** We have tried to make Mei feel welcome.

_______________ **7.** She has told us a great deal about Memphis.

_______________ **8.** We had known Memphis was an important city.

_______________ **9.** However, Mei has described things we never knew!

_______________ **10.** We have decided that we would like to visit Tennessee some day.

B. Complete each sentence with have, has, or had to form the verb tense indicated in parentheses.

1. (present perfect) The pitcher _______________ left the mound.

2. (present perfect) The coach and catcher _______________ talked to him.

3. (past perfect) The coach _______________ warned him to be careful.

4. (present perfect) Jason _______________ taken his place on the mound.

5. (past perfect) Jason _______________ pitched ten games by the end of last season.

6. (present perfect) Jason _______________ pitched very well.

7. (past perfect) The team _______________ won every game last week.

Lesson 38 Using *Is/Are* and *Was/Were*

- Use is and was with a singular subject. EXAMPLE: Here **is** Roberto.
- Use are and were with a plural subject. EXAMPLE: There **are** Dr. Thomas and Dr. Williams.
- Always use are and were with the pronoun you. EXAMPLES: You **are** my favorite cousin. You **are** late today.

- **Circle the verb that agrees with the subject of each sentence.**

1. Here (is, are) the box of paper clips you ordered.
2. There (is, are) three girls named Laura in our apartment building.
3. There (is, are) a small chance of showers tomorrow.
4. Mayor Laroche (is, are) going to speak today.
5. Here (is, are) the tools you asked me to bring.
6. There (is, are) much to be done.
7. Two of these chairs (is, are) damaged.
8. (Is, Are) these cars really being offered for sale?
9. Kelly, (is, are) this your car?
10. Many people (is, are) planning to go to the hockey game.
11. Juan and I (was, were) afraid that Carlos (was, were) not going to arrive on time.
12. Who (was, were) you talking to this afternoon?
13. A group of truck drivers (was, were) in the cafe.
14. There (was, were) many kinds of rare plants in the garden.
15. Several visitors (was, were) here this afternoon.
16. Anita, (wasn't, weren't) you interested in working overtime?
17. Why (wasn't, weren't) these dishes washed last night?
18. The mistakes in punctuation (was, were) carefully checked.
19. Ricardo and Sara (wasn't, weren't) able to help us.
20. There (was, were) two large trays of sandwiches on the picnic table.
21. Each picture for the exhibit (was, were) carefully selected.
22. One of the sisters (was, were) enrolled at a university.
23. Each of the letters (was, were) read aloud.
24. (Was, Were) you planning to go to the park today?
25. Did you know that there (was, were) two new families in our apartment building?
26. (Wasn't, Weren't) you at the annual meeting, Ming?
27. Three of the people (was, were) injured when the accident occurred.
28. (Was, Were) your aunt and uncle the first to build a house on this block?
29. Who (was, were) the first settlers in your community?

Lesson 39 Past Tenses of *Give, Take,* and *Write*

- Never use a helping verb with gave, took, and wrote.
- Always use a helping verb with given, taken, and written.

A. Underline the correct verb.

1. It (took, taken) the mechanic only a few minutes to change the tire.
2. Has anyone (took, taken) my note pad?
3. Who (wrote, written) the best letter?
4. I have (wrote, written) a thank-you note.
5. Tell me who (gave, given) you that address.
6. Have you (gave, given) the dog its food?
7. Bill hadn't (wrote, written) this poem.
8. Have you finally (wrote, written) for the tickets?
9. Emilio had (gave, given) the lecture on boat safety yesterday at the Y.M.C.A.
10. Alicia and I (wrote, written) a letter to the editor.
11. Haven't you (took, taken) your seat yet?
12. We had our picture (took, taken) yesterday.
13. Who (gave, given) you these old magazines?
14. The workers (took, taken) all their equipment with them.
15. A friend had (gave, given) us the furniture.
16. Leslie had (wrote, written) the letter over three weeks ago.
17. Who (took, taken) the most photographs on the trip?
18. The doctor (gave, given) me a tetanus shot after I cut my hand.
19. Has Brian (wrote, written) to Julia yet?

B. Write the correct past tense form of each verb in parentheses to complete the sentences.

1. (take) Amanda recently ____________________ her dog, Ralph, to the veterinarian.
2. (write) The doctor had ____________________ to say that Ralph needed his annual shots.
3. (give) An assistant ____________________ Ralph a dog biscuit as soon as he arrived.
4. (give) That way Ralph was ____________________ something that would distract him.
5. (take) Before Ralph knew it, the doctor had ____________________ a sample of his blood.
6. (take) It only ____________________ a minute to give Ralph his shots.
7. (give) The doctor ____________________ Ralph a pat on the head.
8. (take) "You have ____________________ very good care of Ralph," he said.

Lesson 40 Past Tenses of *See, Go,* and *Begin*

- Never use a helping verb with saw, went, and began.
- Always use a helping verb with seen, gone, and begun.

A. Underline the correct verb.

1. The last person we (saw, seen) in the park was Eric.
2. Who has (went, gone) for the ice?
3. Carla and Yoko (began, begun) to fix the flat tire.
4. Charles (went, gone) to the supermarket for some lettuce.
5. Our summer vacation has (began, begun).
6. They had (saw, seen) a shooting star.
7. Hasn't she (went, gone) to the airport?
8. Yes, we (saw, seen) the concert poster.
9. Alice, have you ever (saw, seen) a penguin?
10. We never (went, gone) to hear the new mayor speak.
11. Olivia, why haven't you (began, begun) your work?
12. Mike (began, begun) to tell us about the accident.
13. Our guests have (went, gone).
14. It (began, begun) to snow early in the evening.
15. Work has finally (began, begun) on the new stadium.
16. We (saw, seen) Pikes Peak last summer.
17. My three sisters (went, gone) to Toronto, Ontario.
18. Have you (saw, seen) the waves pounding the huge boulders?
19. We (went, gone) to hear the symphony last night.
20. They (began, begun) their program with music by Mozart.
21. The program (began, begun) on time.

B. Write a sentence using each verb below.

1. saw ______________________________
2. seen ______________________________
3. gone ______________________________
4. went ______________________________
5. began ______________________________
6. begun ______________________________

Lesson 41

Wear, Rise, Steal, Choose, and *Break*

- Never use a helping verb with wore, rose, stole, chose, and broke.
- Always use a helping verb with worn, risen, stolen, chosen, and broken.

A. Underline the correct verb.

1. We almost froze because we hadn't (wore, worn) coats.
2. Haven't you (chose, chosen) a new shirt?
3. I (broke, broken) my new bike.
4. The river (rose, risen) two feet during the night.
5. Someone had (stole, stolen) our car last week.
6. Juanita had (chose, chosen) many of our old landmarks for the city tour.
7. I have (wore, worn) these uncomfortable shoes for the last time.
8. We were miles along the way when the sun (rose, risen).
9. The squirrels have (stole, stolen) most of our acorns.
10. The airplane (rose, risen) above the clouds.
11. The children have (wore, worn) a path through the backyard.
12. They (chose, chosen) to stay at the camp for a day.
13. Jan had (broke, broken) her leg the summer we visited her.
14. Have you ever (stole, stolen) home base?
15. Our pizza dough had (rose, risen) by the time we sliced the pepperoni.
16. The bottle's protective seal was (broke, broken), so we returned it to the store.
17. Kurt and Jamie (wore, worn) each other's clothes when they were younger.
18. The full moon had (rose, risen) over the deep, dark lake.
19. The jewel thief (stole, stolen) one too many diamonds before he got caught.

B. Circle any mistakes in the use of past tense verbs.

The sun had just rose when Kate recognized the familiar sound of fishing boats returning to shore. She hadn't meant to sleep late this morning, but the early morning waves had coaxed her back to sleep. Now, slipping into her sweatshirt, shoes, and damp shorts, Kate noticed that seagulls had again stole fish from the pail of bait. She chuckled at the thought, and then tossed the circling birds another minnow. Turning, Kate noticed Luke nearing the boat. He worn the same windbreaker and soft, leather shoes nearly every day since they first met, months ago. Kate paused for a moment. It occurred to her that she chosen a good friend. Luke had never broke a shoestring, or a promise.

Come, Ring, Drink, Know, and *Throw*

- Never use a helping verb with came, rang, drank, knew, and threw.
- Always use a helping verb with come, rung, drunk, known, and thrown.

A. Underline the correct verb.

1. The tired horse (drank, drunk) from the cool stream.
2. The church bell has not (rang, rung) today.
3. I haven't (drank, drunk) my hot chocolate.
4. We (knew, known) that it was time to go.
5. Have you (threw, thrown) the garbage out?
6. Haven't the movers (came, come) for our furniture?
7. We (rang, rung) the fire alarm five minutes ago.
8. Haven't you (know, known) him for a long time?
9. I (threw, thrown) the ball to James.
10. My friends from London, England, (came, come) this afternoon.
11. Why haven't you (drank, drunk) your juice?
12. I always (came, come) to work in my wheelchair now.
13. I (knew, known) Pat when she was just a child.
14. Have you (threw, thrown) away last week's newspaper?
15. We have (came, come) to tell you something.
16. If you already (rang, rung) the bell, then you might try knocking.
17. Tony thinks he (drank, drunk) something that made him ill.

B. Write a sentence using each verb below.

1. came ______________________________
2. come ______________________________
3. rang ______________________________
4. rung ______________________________
5. threw ______________________________
6. thrown ______________________________
7. drank ______________________________
8. drunk ______________________________
9. knew ______________________________

Lesson 43 Eat, Fall, Draw, Drive, and Run

- Never use a helping verb with ate, fell, drew, drove, and ran.
- Always use a helping verb with eaten, fallen, drawn, driven, and run.

A. Underline the correct verb.

1. Taro, have you (drew, drawn) your diagram?
2. When we had (drove, driven) for two hours, we (began, begun) to feel hungry.
3. All of our pears have (fell, fallen) from the tree.
4. After we had (ate, eaten) our dinner, we (ran, run) around the lake.
5. A great architect (drew, drawn) the plans for our civic center.
6. We had just (ran, run) into the house when we saw our friends.
7. Hadn't the building already (fell, fallen) when you (ran, run) around the corner?
8. Those heavy curtains in the theater have (fell, fallen) down.
9. Last week we (drove, driven) to the lake for a vacation.
10. I have just (ate, eaten) a delicious slice of pizza.
11. I (ate, eaten) my breakfast before six o'clock this morning.
12. All of the leaves have (fell, fallen) from the elm trees.
13. When was the last time you (ran, run) a mile?

B. Write the correct past tense form of each verb in parentheses to complete the sentences.

1. (drive) Last weekend we ________________ to the lake for a picnic.
2. (draw) Since Jenna knew several shortcuts, she ________________ a detailed map for us.
3. (fall) She mentioned that during a recent summer storm, debris had ________________ on many of the roads.
4. (fall) She warned us that a large tree ________________ on one of the main roads.
5. (drive) Jenna claimed that she had never ________________ under such dangerous circumstances.
6. (run) "I almost ________________ right into that tree in the dark!" Jenna said.
7. (eat) In order to avoid traveling at night, we ________________ our dinner after we got home from the lake.
8. (eat) We had ________________ so much during our picnic that none of us minded waiting!
9. (draw) Once home, we all agreed that Jenna had ________________ a great map for us.
10. (run) We made the trip in record time, and we hadn't ________________ over any trees in the process!

Lesson 44 Forms of *Do*

- Never use a helping verb with did.
  EXAMPLE: Anne **did** a great job on her test.
- Always use a helping verb with done.
  EXAMPLE: Hallie **had** also **done** a great job.
- Doesn't is the contraction of does not. Use it with singular nouns and the pronouns he, she, and it.
  EXAMPLES: Rachel **doesn't** want to go. It **doesn't** seem right.
- Don't is the contraction of do not. Use it with plural nouns and with the pronouns I, you, we, and they.
  EXAMPLES: Mr. and Mrs. Ricci **don't** live there. You **don't** have your purse.

A. Underline the correct verb.

1. Why (doesn't, don't) Lois have the car keys?
2. Show me the way you (did, done) it.
3. Have the three of you (did, done) most of the work?
4. Why (doesn't, don't) she cash a check today?
5. Please show me what damage the storm (did, done).
6. (Doesn't, Don't) the workers on the morning shift do a fine job?
7. Have the new owners of our building (did, done) anything about the plumbing?
8. (Doesn't, Don't) those apples look overly ripe?
9. Chris (doesn't, don't) want to do the spring cleaning this week.
10. The gloves and the hat (doesn't, don't) match.
11. Carolyn, have you (did, done) your homework today?
12. Who (did, done) this fine job of painting?
13. (Doesn't, Don't) the tile in our new kitchen look nice?
14. (Doesn't, Don't) that dog stay in a fenced yard?
15. He has (did, done) me a great favor.
16. I will help if he (doesn't, don't).

B. Write one sentence using did and one sentence using done.

1. ______________________________

2. ______________________________

C. Write one sentence using doesn't and one sentence using don't.

1. ______________________________

2. ______________________________

Lesson 45 Transitive and Intransitive Verbs

- There are two kinds of action verbs: **transitive** and **intransitive.**
- A transitive verb has a direct object.

  D.O.
  EXAMPLE: Jeffrey **painted** the house.
- An intransitive verb does not need an object to complete its meaning.

  EXAMPLES: The sun **rises** in the east. She **walks** quickly.

A. Underline the verb in each sentence. Then write T for transitive or I for intransitive.

_______ 1. Kristina joined the health club in March.

_______ 2. She wanted the exercise to help her stay healthy.

_______ 3. Kristina exercised every day after work.

_______ 4. She became friends with Nancy.

_______ 5. They worked out together.

_______ 6. Nancy preferred the treadmill.

_______ 7. Kristina liked aerobics and running.

_______ 8. Sometimes they switched activities.

_______ 9. Nancy took an aerobics class.

_______ 10. Kristina used the treadmill.

_______ 11. Occasionally they swam in the pool.

_______ 12. Nancy was the better swimmer.

_______ 13. But Kristina had more fun.

_______ 14. She just splashed around in the water.

B. Underline the transitive verb, and circle the direct object in each sentence.

1. Carlos walked Tiny every day.
2. Tiny usually pulled Carlos along.
3. Carlos washed Tiny every other week.
4. Tiny loved water.
5. He splashed Carlos whenever he could.
6. Tiny also loved rawhide bones.
7. He chewed the bones until they were gone.
8. Carlos found Tiny when Tiny was just a puppy.

Lesson 46 Verbals

- A **verbal** is a verb form that functions as a noun or adjective. There are three types of verbals: **infinitives, participles,** and **gerunds.**
- An **infinitive** is the base form of the verb, commonly preceded by to. An infinitive that functions as a noun is a verbal.
  EXAMPLE: The object of the game is **to win.**
- A present or past **participle** that functions as an adjective is a verbal.
  EXAMPLES: A **running** horse galloped down the road. **Dried** leaves flew from his hooves.
- A **gerund** is the present participle of a verb form ending in -ing that is used as a noun.
  EXAMPLE: **Skiing** is her favorite sport.

A. Underline the infinitive in each sentence below.

1. Alan refused to quit.
2. The only thing he wanted was to finish.
3. Alan had trained to run this race for months.
4. It was not important to win.
5. Alan simply needed to finish.
6. He hoped to accomplish his goal.
7. Soon he was close enough to see the finish line.

B. Underline the participle in each sentence below.

1. A yelling cheerleader led the crowd.
2. The excited crowd roared.
3. The running team took the field.
4. The marching band started to play.
5. Chosen members of the band flashed cards.
6. The flashing cards spelled a message.
7. The interested students studied hard.

C. Underline the gerund in each sentence below.

1. Studying is an important job.
2. Language arts and reading help improve your language ability.
3. Learning can be rewarding.
4. Memorizing is another skill you can learn.
5. Remembering is not always easy.
6. Do you think studying is time well spent?
7. Dancing is Lauren's favorite activity.

D. Underline the verbal in each sentence, and write infinitive, participle, or gerund on the line.

_______________ 1. To act in a play is an honor.

_______________ 2. Acting can be very exciting.

_______________ 3. To write plays takes a lot of skill.

_______________ 4. Working in the theater is interesting.

_______________ 5. Sally wanted to participate.

_______________ 6. The hurried director got ready for the auditions.

_______________ 7. Sally prepared a moving scene.

_______________ 8. She was finally ready to read her scene.

_______________ 9. Auditioning can scare anyone.

_______________ 10. Sally's stirring performance won her a part.

_______________ 11. Rehearsing can take up much time.

_______________ 12. The actors must work long hours to memorize their parts.

_______________ 13. Sally's convincing performance was outstanding.

_______________ 14. All of the actors excelled in performing.

_______________ 15. The smiling director congratulated the cast.

_______________ 16. "To act is an art," said the director.

_______________ 17. He called them all budding artists.

_______________ 18. Performing is a pleasure for Yolanda.

_______________ 19. Bowing is even more fun.

_______________ 20. The audience could tell by Yolanda's face that she enjoyed playing the part.

_______________ 21. To continue her studies is her goal.

_______________ 22. Acting is very important to Yolanda and Sally.

_______________ 23. Interrupted lessons would distress them both.

_______________ 24. They are consumed with acting.

_______________ 25. They need constant practice to excel.

_______________ 26. Well-rehearsed actors perform better.

Lesson 47 Active and Passive Voice

- **Voice** refers to the relation of a subject to its verb.
- In the **active voice,** the subject acts.
  EXAMPLE: **I painted** the house.
- In the **passive voice,** the subject receives the action.
  EXAMPLE: The house **was painted** by me.
- Only transitive verbs are used in the passive voice.

A. Write A if the sentence is in the active voice and P if it is in the passive voice.

_______ **1.** Marty applied for a job in a grocery store.

_______ **2.** He needs money for gas and car repairs.

_______ **3.** He will handle the cash register.

_______ **4.** Marty will also stock the shelves.

_______ **5.** The application was turned in last week.

_______ **6.** The store's manager reads every application.

_______ **7.** Then the applicants are interviewed.

_______ **8.** Marty was interviewed on Monday.

_______ **9.** The manager was impressed by Marty.

_______ **10.** He will give Marty the job.

B. Rewrite each sentence in the active voice.

1. Kate was given a job babysitting by the McNeils.

____

2. The children will be watched by her every day.

____

3. Kate will be driven to their house by her friend.

____

C. Rewrite each sentence in the passive voice.

1. Trina plays the drums in the band.

____

2. She chose the drums because her father played drums.

____

3. Trina won an award for her playing.

____

Lesson 48 Pronouns

- A **subject pronoun** is used in the subject of a sentence and after a linking verb.
  EXAMPLES: **We** are going to the tournament. The woman in the suit is **she.**
- An **object pronoun** is used after an action verb or a preposition.
  EXAMPLE: James threw the ball to **me.**
- A **possessive pronoun** is used to show ownership of something.
  EXAMPLES: The red shoes are **mine.** Those are **my** red shoes.
- An **indefinite pronoun** does not refer to a specific person or thing.
  EXAMPLE: **Someone** should take that history class.
- Use who as a subject pronoun, and use whom as an object pronoun.
  EXAMPLES: **Who** is going to the party? We will ask **whom** to go with us?

A. Underline each correct pronoun.

1. Stephanie spoke to Jennifer and (I, me) about it.

2. Dean sent Tom and (they, them) some new shirts.

3. Please bring Anne and (I, me) some cool water.

4. Here comes (my, me) brother David.

5. Susan and (he, him) were late today.

6. Was it (she, her) who answered the knock?

7. I don't believe it was (they, them)!

8. Mona took Doug and (we, us) to work.

9. He told Steven and (she, her) about the problem.

10. Don't you think (someone, us) should help?

11. Rosa and (I, me) are going to work until seven o'clock.

12. It wasn't (your, yours) cat that meowed.

13. (He, Him) and Calvin are going to the game.

14. She told Kate and (my, me) about her fishing trip.

15. (Who, Whom) did you say got here early?

16. He said that it was (they, them) who came to our house.

17. (Everyone, We) will carry his or her own bundles.

18. It was (they, their) babysitter who knocked on the door.

19. (Who, Whom) did you meet for lunch?

20. Elizabeth and (she, her) always sit together.

21. This sweater is (hers, she).

22. (Who, Whom) led the band in the parade?

23. The red car is (our, ours).

24. Can you predict (who, whom) will win the election?

B. Underline each pronoun.

1. I told you to speak to him about our fishing trip.
2. Who is speaking?
3. They saw us when we passed by their house.
4. Just between you and me, I want to go with them.
5. He and Mike are going with us.
6. My decision to leave was made before our conversation.
7. Whom did you see?
8. This package was sent to you and me.
9. They are going with us to the game.
10. Jerry broke his arm.
11. Who told them?
12. She is my friend who moved to Mexico.
13. This check is mine.
14. Someone took some fresh flowers to them.
15. Who is she?
16. She went with us to the parade.
17. John, who is the president of that company?
18. Will she go with you?
19. Who telephoned me?
20. Should we eat with them at the picnic?
21. Which is your raincoat?
22. Did I tell you about our plans?
23. Which is mine?
24. Do you recall your sister's middle initial?
25. Why can't you come with us?
26. Did anybody get a letter?
27. You and I are on the list, too.
28. Did you see him?

C. Write sentences using the following pronouns:

1. theirs ______________________________
2. you and I ______________________________
3. you and me ______________________________
4. them ______________________________
5. anyone ______________________________

Antecedents

- An **antecedent** is the word to which a pronoun refers.
  EXAMPLE: **Dogs** are dangerous if **they** bite.
- A pronoun must agree with its antecedent in **gender, (masculine, feminine,** or **neuter)** and in **number** (singular or plural).
  EXAMPLES: **Sally** washed **her** hair. The **storm** changed **its** course.
  The **workers** went to **their** offices.
- If the antecedent is an indefinite pronoun (one that doesn't refer to a specific person or thing), it is correct to use a masculine pronoun. However, it is now common to use both a masculine and a feminine pronoun.
  EXAMPLES: **Someone** lost **his** gloves. **Someone** lost **his or her** gloves.

A. Underline each pronoun. Circle its antecedent.

1. Mike said he would tutor Carmen.
2. Carmen was doing poorly in her math class.
3. Carmen often shakes her head in confusion.
4. Mike promised to try his hardest.
5. Carmen worked on her math, but it was difficult.
6. Mike and Carmen said they would work every night.
7. The math test was coming, and it promised to be hard.
8. The class was ready for its test.
9. Carmen's palms were sweaty, and they felt clammy.
10. The teacher said he knew Carmen would do well.
11. When Carmen started the test, it didn't seem so hard.
12. Each student finished his or her test and put it on the instructor's desk.
13. The instructor would correct the tests and hand them back.
14. Carmen was pleased with her grade.

B. Circle the pronoun in parentheses that agrees with the antecedent.

1. Earl and Leon practiced (their, his) free throws.
2. Each hoped practice would make (him, her) play better.
3. The team held (its, their) practice every day.
4. Leon practiced (his, their) passing.
5. It is important to study the plays because (they, he) must be remembered.
6. Carl waxed (him, his) car.
7. The building was closed because (its, their) windows were damaged in the storm.
8. The flowers opened (its, their) petals in the sunshine.
9. Maggie found (his, her) book in the closet.
10. The guests piled (their, them) coats on the table.

Lesson 50 Adjectives

- An **adjective** is a word that modifies a noun or a pronoun.
  EXAMPLE: He likes **chocolate** cookies.
- Adjectives usually tell **what kind, which one,** or **how many.**
  EXAMPLES: **bright** penny, **these** oranges, **twelve** classmates
- A **proper adjective** is an adjective that is formed from a proper noun. It always begins with a capital letter.
  EXAMPLES: **Asian** continent, **English** language
- The articles a, an, and the are called **limiting adjectives.**

A. Write three adjectives to describe each noun.

1. mountains ______ ______ ______
2. weather ______ ______ ______
3. journey ______ ______ ______
4. classroom ______ ______ ______
5. book ______ ______ ______

B. Underline each adjective.

1. This old chair is comfortable.
2. We have read a funny story recently.
3. This heavy traffic creates many dangerous situations.
4. The eager sailors collected odd souvenirs at every port.
5. The tired, thirsty soldiers marched on.
6. This is my favorite book.
7. The solitary guard walked along the lonely beach.
8. We sat in the sixth row.
9. These damp matches will not strike.
10. Dan made French toast for breakfast.
11. Will you light those candles, please?
12. A red bird chirped loudly in the tall tree.
13. The heavy elephant sat down slowly.
14. A tour bus stopped at the pirate's cove.
15. The gorgeous model wore Italian leather.
16. We ate fresh seafood on our vacation.
17. Do you like mashed or baked potatoes?
18. She served Chinese food for dinner.

Lesson 51 Demonstrative Adjectives

- A **demonstrative adjective** is one that points out a specific person or thing.
- This and that modify singular nouns. This points to a person or thing nearby, and that points to a person or thing farther away.
  EXAMPLES: **This** movie is my favorite. **That** sign is difficult to see.
- These and those modify plural nouns. These points to persons or things nearby and those points to persons or things farther away.
  EXAMPLES: **These** ribbons are the most colorful.
  Those towels need to be folded.
- The word them is a pronoun. Never use it to describe a noun.

Underline the correct demonstrative adjective.

1. Move (those, them) plants inside since it may freeze tonight.
2. (These, That) box in front of me is too heavy to lift.
3. Who brought us (those, them) delicious cookies?
4. Look at (those, them) playful kittens.
5. (That, Those) kind of friend is appreciated.
6. (Those, Them) pictures are beautiful.
7. What are (those, them) sounds I hear?
8. Did you ever meet (those, them) people?
9. We have just developed (these, them) photographs.
10. Do you know any of (those, them) young people?
11. May we take some of (these, them) folders?
12. I have been looking over (these, them) magazines.
13. Do not eat too many of (those, them) peaches.
14. I do not like (this, these) kind of syrup.
15. (Those, Them) people should be served next.
16. Jimmy, please mail (these, them) letters.
17. Look at (those, them) posters I made!
18. (This, That) suburb is fifty miles away.
19. (These, Them) antique coins are valuable.
20. Look at (those, that) soccer players hustle!
21. José, may we see (these, them) photographs?
22. Please return (that, these) library books.
23. (These, Them) clothes need to be washed.
24. Please hand me (that, those) plates.
25. (Those, Them) cookies have nuts in them.

Lesson 52 Comparing with Adjectives

- An adjective has three degrees of comparison: **positive, comparative,** and **superlative.**
- The simple form of the adjective is called the **positive** degree.
  EXAMPLE: Ian is **short.**
- When two people or things are being compared, the **comparative** degree is used.
  EXAMPLE: Ian is **shorter** than Lee.
- When three or more people or things are being compared, the **superlative** degree is used.
  EXAMPLE: Ian is the **shortest** person in the group.
- For all adjectives of one syllable and a few adjectives of two syllables, add -er to form the comparative degree, and -est to form the superlative degree.
  EXAMPLE: smart—smarter—smartest
- For some adjectives of two syllables and all adjectives of three or more syllables, use more or less to form the comparative and most or least to form the superlative.
  EXAMPLES: This test is **more** difficult than I expected. Carol is the **most** generous of all. Kate is **less** talkative than Tom. Mary is the **least** talkative of all.

- **Complete each sentence with the correct degree of comparison of the adjective given in parentheses. Some of the forms are irregular.**

1. (changeable) The weather seems ______________________ this year than last.
2. (faithful) I think the dog is the ______________________ of all animals.
3. (agreeable) Is James ______________________ than Sam?
4. (busy) Theresa is the ______________________ person in the office.
5. (long) Which is the ______________________ river, the Mississippi or the Amazon?
6. (lovely) I think the rose is the ______________________ of all flowers.
7. (fresh) Show me the ______________________ cookies in the store.
8. (high) Which of the two mountains is ______________________?
9. (enjoyable) Which is the ______________________, television or the movies?
10. (reckless) That person is the ______________________ driver in town.
11. (young) Of all the players, Maria is the ______________________.
12. (tall) Alberto is the ______________________ of the three men.
13. (difficult) Isn't the seventh problem ______________________ than the eighth?
14. (quiet) We have found the ______________________ spot in the park.

Lesson 53 Adverbs

- An **adverb** is a word that modifies a verb, an adjective, or another adverb.
  EXAMPLES: The rain poured **steadily.** His memories were **extremely** vivid. She responded **very** quickly.
- An adverb usually tells **how, when, where,** or **how often.**
- Many adverbs end in -ly.

A. Underline each adverb.

1. The person read slowly but clearly and expressively.
2. Adam, you are driving too recklessly.
3. The airplane started moving slowly but quickly gained speed.
4. I spoke too harshly to my friends.
5. How did all of you get here?
6. I looked everywhere for my pen.
7. The man stopped suddenly and quickly turned around.
8. Stacy read that poem too rapidly.
9. Janice plays the guitar well.
10. The child was sleeping soundly.
11. The car was running noisily.
12. We returned early.
13. Those trees were severely damaged in the fire.
14. Jack ran quickly, but steadily, in the race.

B. Write two adverbs that could be used to modify each verb.

1. read ______________________ ______________________
2. think ______________________ ______________________
3. walk ______________________ ______________________
4. eat ______________________ ______________________
5. sing ______________________ ______________________
6. speak ______________________ ______________________
7. dive ______________________ ______________________
8. study ______________________ ______________________
9. write ______________________ ______________________
10. look ______________________ ______________________

Lesson 54 Comparing with Adverbs

- An **adverb** has three degrees of comparison: **positive, comparative,** and **superlative.**
- The simple form of the adverb is called the **positive** degree.
  EXAMPLE: Kathy ran **fast** in the race.
- When two actions are being compared, the **comparative** degree is used.
  EXAMPLE: Amy ran **faster** than Kathy.
- When three or more actions are being compared, the **superlative** degree is used.
  EXAMPLE: Maureen ran the **fastest** of all.
- Use -er to form the comparative degree and use -est to form the superlative degree of one-syllable adverbs.
- Use more or most with longer adverbs and with adverbs that end in -ly.
  EXAMPLES: Louisa ran **more energetically** than Bob.
  Ms. Baker ran the **most energetically** of all the runners.

A. Underline the adverb that best completes each sentence.

1. Mark arrived (sooner, soonest) than Greg.
2. Tony arrived the (sooner, soonest) of all.
3. They had to work very (hard, harder, hardest).
4. Tony painted (more, most) carefully than Mark.
5. Mark worked (faster, fastest) than Greg, so Mark painted the walls.
6. Lauren worked the (more, most) carefully of all.

B. Complete each sentence with the proper form of the adverb in parentheses.

1. (fast) Jason wanted to be the ____________________ runner at our school.
2. (fast) Juan could run ____________________ than Jason.
3. (seriously) Jason trained ____________________ than he had before.
4. (frequently) Jason is on the track ____________________ of all the runners.
5. (quickly) Jason ran the sprint ____________________ than he did yesterday.
6. (promptly) Jason arrives for practice ____________________ of anyone on the team.
7. (promptly) He even arrives ____________________ than the coach!
8. (eagerly) Juan does warm-up exercises ____________________ of all the runners.
9. (carefully) Who concentrates ____________________ on his timing, Juan or Jason?
10. (hard) The coach congratulates Jason on being the player who works the

____________________.

Prepositions

- A **preposition** is a word that shows the relationship of a noun or a pronoun to another word in the sentence.
  EXAMPLES: The child ran **into** the **house.** He put his boots **under** the **table.**
- These are some commonly used prepositions:

about	against	at	between	from	of	through	under
above	among	behind	by	in	on	to	upon
across	around	beside	for	into	over	toward	with

- **Underline each preposition in the sentences below.**

1. Can you draw a map of your area?
2. Who is the owner of this car?
3. The pecan is a common tree in the South.
4. For whom are you waiting?
5. At the meeting, he spoke to me about your athletic ability.
6. Our company is proud of its industrious employees.
7. Her friend Cynthia stood beside her.
8. A small amount of that soup is all I want.
9. We went to the house at the end of the street.
10. There were seventy-five post offices in the United States in 1790.
11. Most of the spectators stood during the last quarter of the game.
12. These shoes of mine are too tight at the heel.
13. We ate dinner at the new restaurant near the river.
14. They stood on the porch and watched for the mail carrier.
15. Anyone can succeed with hard work.
16. We walked behind that group.
17. Astronaut Sally Ride was the first woman in space.
18. A group of people on horses rode behind the band.
19. We walked to the picnic grounds during the lunch hour.
20. Ben slid down the slippery hill.
21. There is a bridge across the river in our town.
22. The ball was knocked over the fence and into the pond.
23. I see a spot of dirt under your left eye.
24. One can observe a strange world below the surface of an ocean.
25. The rocket quickly disappeared behind the clouds.
26. Much of our land is drained by the Mississippi River.
27. Please sit between us.
28. This package is for you.

Lesson 56 Prepositional Phrases

- A **phrase** is a group of closely related words used as a single part of speech but not containing a subject and predicate.
  EXAMPLE: The writer **of this novel** is signing autographs.
- A **prepositional phrase** is a group of words that begins with a preposition and ends with a noun or pronoun.
  EXAMPLE: He took the train **to New York.**
- The noun or pronoun in the prepositional phrase is called the **object of the preposition.**
  EXAMPLE: He took the train to **New York.**

- **Put parentheses around each prepositional phrase. Then underline each preposition, and circle the object of the preposition.**

1. The airplane was flying (above the clouds).
2. We are moving to North Carolina.
3. Sandra lives on the second block.
4. An old water tower once stood on that hill.
5. The car slid on the wet pavement.
6. Sealing wax was invented in the seventeenth century.
7. Motto rings were first used by the Romans.
8. Tungsten, a metal, was discovered in 1781.
9. Roses originally came from Asia.
10. The ball rolled into the street.
11. Do you always keep the puppies in a pen?
12. The children climbed over the fence.
13. She lives in Denver, Colorado.
14. Columbus made three trips to North America.
15. They spread the lunch under the shade of the giant elm tree.
16. The treasure was found by a scuba diver.
17. A squad of soldiers marched behind the tank.
18. Shall I row across the stream?
19. Large airplanes fly across the nation.
20. Walter looked into the sack.
21. The cat ran up the pole.
22. We visited the Alexander Graham Bell Museum in Nova Scotia.
23. Many tourists come to our region.
24. We spent last summer in the Adirondack Mountains.
25. Do not stand behind a parked car.

Lesson 57

Prepositional Phrases as Adjectives and Adverbs

- A prepositional phrase can be used to describe a noun or a pronoun. Then the prepositional phrase is being used as an **adjective** to tell which one, what kind, or how many.
  EXAMPLE: The bird **in the tree** whistled.
  The prepositional phrase in the tree tells **which** bird.
- A prepositional phrase can be used to describe a verb. Then the prepositional phrase is being used as an **adverb** to tell how, where, or when.
  EXAMPLE: Charlie ate breakfast **before leaving for school.**
  The prepositional phrase **before leaving for school** tells **when** Charlie ate breakfast.

- **Underline each prepositional phrase, and classify it as adjective or adverb.**

1. They went to the ranch. (adv.)
2. The first savings bank was established in France.
3. Fall Creek Falls in Tennessee is my home.
4. Return all books to the public library.
5. Mark lives in an old house.
6. Tanya bought a sweater with red trim.
7. The birds in the zoo are magnificent.
8. Jade is found in Myanmar.
9. I spent the remainder of my money.
10. The magician waved a wand over the hat, and a rabbit appeared.
11. The diameter of a Sequoia tree trunk can reach ten feet.
12. The capital of New York is Albany.
13. The narrowest streets are near the docks.
14. Our family went to the movie.
15. Roald Amundsen discovered the South Pole in 1911.
16. The floor in this room is painted black.
17. The dead leaves are blowing across the yard.
18. A forest of petrified wood has been found.
19. The mole's tunnel runs across the lawn.

Lesson 58 Conjunctions

- A **conjunction** is a word used to join words or groups of words.
  EXAMPLES: Yuri **and** Brant have arrived. They worked **until** the sun went down.
- These are some commonly used conjunctions:

although	because	however	or	that	when	whereas
and	but	if	since	though	whether	yet
as	for	nor	than	unless	while	

- Some conjunctions are used in pairs. These include either . . . or, neither . . . nor, and not only . . . but also.

Underline each conjunction in the sentences below.

1. Do you know whether Brandon is going to the employment office?
2. Jesse, are you and Ryan going to see a movie this afternoon?
3. Linda will go to the coast when the weather turns warm.
4. Gina or Vicki will take me to practice.
5. Are you and Elizabeth going swimming this Saturday?
6. Paul will be here unless he has to work.
7. Dean or I must go to the supermarket.
8. Chicken and potatoes are my favorite foods.
9. The trainer and the animals gave a good show.
10. I was angry at Megan because she was not on time.
11. Tom gets into trouble, but he usually gets out of it.
12. Carelessness is the cause of many falls and burns.
13. She stopped work because she had to leave early.
14. Matt has been understanding since I started working two jobs.
15. This chair is small, but it is comfortable.
16. Although it looked like rain, we went for a drive.
17. Kerry is two years older than Tom.
18. The remark was neither just nor kind.
19. You may go either by bus or by plane.
20. Tim is here, but he is too busy to help us right now.
21. Let's go inside, for it is getting dark.
22. We listened closely while the directions were given.
23. Fruit is not only delicious, but also healthful.
24. Bring either a short poem or a rhyme to class tomorrow.
25. Anne neither asked for help nor received any.
26. Neither Joe nor Marie went to the show.

Review

A. Write the part of speech above each underlined word. Use the abbreviations given in the box.

n.	noun
pron.	pronoun
v.	verb
adj.	adjective
adv.	adverb
prep.	preposition
conj.	conjunction

1. A heavy dust storm rolled across the prairie.
2. This is a nice surprise!
3. The dark clouds slowly gathered in the north.
4. Marlee and I are showing slides of the photographs that we took on our trip.
5. Is the capital of your state built on a river?
6. These shrubs are beautiful.
7. Someone opened the door very cautiously and tiptoed inside.
8. Please handle this extremely fragile china very carefully.
9. The weary people waited for the long parade to start.
10. Large herds of longhorn cattle grazed on these vast plains.
11. We are going to the new mall today, but Sara can't go with us.
12. Floyd, you are eating that food too rapidly.

B. Write the plural form or the possessive form of the noun in parentheses.

1. (bench) The park ______________________ need to be painted.
2. (fly) The ______________________ landed on our picnic lunch.
3. (hero) All of the ______________________ medals were awarded at the ceremony.
4. (pony) Her ______________________ saddle has been cleaned and oiled.
5. (watch) My ______________________ hands stopped moving.

C. Underline the appositive or appositive phrase, and circle the noun it identifies.

1. We plan to visit Ottawa, the capital of Canada, on our vacation.
2. My older sister Kira is an engineer.
3. We ate a hearty breakfast, pancakes and ham, before going to work.

D. Circle the correct verb.

1. A former resident (gave, given) this fountain to the city.
2. Was it the telephone or the doorbell that (rang, rung)?
3. Our guest speaker has (come, came) a little early.
4. Caroline has (know, known) Paul for ten years.
5. We asked Jan to (drive, driven) us to the movies.
6. Matt, haven't you (ate, eaten) the last piece of pineapple cake?
7. The frightened deer (ran, run) into the forest.
8. The Arnolds (gone, went) to Florida last January.
9. Andy (doesn't, don't) like to be late to work.
10. Chloe (took, taken) her brother to the zoo.
11. Susan (did, done) all of her chores before we went to the movie.
12. Jessica and I (is, are) ready to go, too.
13. Many of the trout (was, were) returned to the stream after the contest.
14. I have (began, begun) the study of Spanish.
15. A dead silence had (fell, fallen) upon the listeners.
16. Larry (wasn't, weren't) at work this morning.

E. Underline the verbal in each sentence, and write infinitive, participle, or gerund on the line.

_______________ 1. The reason they went to the lake was to fish.

_______________ 2. Skating has become a popular sport.

_______________ 3. The flashing lights warned people of danger.

_______________ 4. Juan's goal is to finish law school.

_______________ 5. The improved detergent cleaned better than the old formula.

F. Underline the pronoun in parentheses that agrees with the antecedent. Circle the antecedent.

1. Curtis and Erika tutored Mark because (he, they) had missed the review.
2. The office workers had to leave (their, its) building when a fire started.
3. Bob and Andre brought the posters to (them, their) campaign office.
4. My sister collected baskets on (her, their) trip to Mexico.
5. The volunteers accepted donations and gave (it, them) to the charity.

Using What You've Learned

A. Read the following paragraph.

Amelia Earhart was born in Atchinson, Kansas, in 1897. She is one of the most famous American aviators. She was the first woman to fly solo across the Atlantic Ocean. At the time, 1932, air travel was a very rare occurrence, and it was even more unusual for women. With Earhart's example and encouragement, women were just beginning to break into aviation.

One of her most daring flights was a solo trip from Hawaii to California in 1935. That journey was a longer and more dangerous flight than her European trip. However, it was for her attempted around-the-world flight in 1937 that most people remember Earhart. During this flight, her plane disappeared somewhere in the South Pacific. She and her co-pilot were never found. Many people believe she was working as a United States spy to gather information on the Japanese war movement, but this idea has never been proven.

B. In the paragraph above, find three different pronouns and write them on the lines below.

1. ____________ 2. ____________ 3. ____________

C. Find two proper adjectives and the nouns they describe.

1. ____________ 2. ____________

D. Find two demonstrative adjectives and the nouns they describe.

1. ____________ 2. ____________

E. Find two comparative adjectives.

1. ____________ 2. ____________

F. Find six prepositional phrases.

1. ____________
2. ____________
3. ____________
4. ____________
5. ____________
6. ____________

G. Find three conjunctions.

1. ____________ 2. ____________ 3. ____________

H. Rewrite the following paragraphs. Correct any mistakes in the use of possessive and plural nouns, pronouns, and verbs.

The first pilots of a motor-powered airplane was the Wright brothers, Orville and Wilbur. On December 17, 1903, the Wrights successfully flown their plane, Flyer I for the first time. The gasoline-powered plane were in the air for a total of 12 seconds. Another flight that day last 59 seconds and gone 852 feet.

The Wright brothers spent many years perfecting his airplane designs. Them were gifted engineer's and already has build printing machinery, bicycles, and gliders. Their breakthrough come when them observing the way a buzzard control their flight. Them continued to improve on its airplane designs over the next few years. They eventually sells the first military airplane to the United State Army in 1909. Eventually, European mechanic's produced more advanced airplane than the Wrights airplanes.

Lesson 59 Using Capital Letters

- **Capitalize** the first word of a sentence and of each line of poetry.
  EXAMPLES: Jim recited a poem. The first two lines follow.
  All the animals looked up in wonder
  When they heard the roaring thunder.
- Capitalize the first word of a direct quotation.
  EXAMPLE: Beth said, "Let's try to memorize a poem, too."
- Capitalize the first, last, and all important words in the titles of books, poems, stories, and songs.
  EXAMPLES: *The Jungle Book,* "Snow Time"

A. Circle each letter that should be capitalized. Write the capital letter above it.

1. Anthony said, "what time does the movie start?"
2. francis Scott Key wrote "the star spangled banner."
3. edgar Allan Poe, the author of "the raven," was born in Boston.
4. paul asked, "when do you plan to visit your friend?"
5. who wrote the poems "snowbound" and "the barefoot boy"?
6. what famous American said, "give me liberty, or give me death"?

- Capitalize all **proper nouns.**
  EXAMPLES: James T. White, Mother, Fifth Avenue, Italy, Missouri Smokey Mountains, Thanksgiving, November, Statue of Liberty, *Mayflower,* British Columbia
- Capitalize all **proper adjectives.** A proper adjective is an adjective that is made from a proper noun.
  EXAMPLES: the Italian language, Chinese food, French tourists

B. Circle each letter that should be capitalized. Write the capital letter above it.

1. Lauren, does your friend live in miami, florida, or atlanta, georgia?
2. The potomac river forms the boundary between virginia and maryland.
3. The *pinta,* the *niña,* and the *santa maría* were the ships columbus sailed.
4. The spanish explorers discovered the mississippi river before the english settlers landed at jamestown.
5. The founder of the american red cross was clara barton.
6. Glaciers are found in the rocky mountains, the andes mountains, and the alps.

- Capitalize a person's title when it comes before a name.
  EXAMPLES: Mayor Flynn, Doctor Suarez, Governor Kuhn
- Capitalize abbreviations of titles.
  EXAMPLES: Ms. C. Cooke, Dr. Pearsoll, Gov. Milne, Judge Brenner

C. Circle each letter that should be capitalized. Write the capital letter above it.

1. How long have you been seeing dr. thompson?
2. Our class invited mayor thomas to speak at graduation.
3. dr. crawford w. long of Georgia is believed to be the first physician to use ether during surgery.
4. What time do you expect mr. and mrs. randall to arrive?
5. Most people believe senator dixon will win reelection.
6. It will be a close election unless gov. alden gives his support.
7. When is ms. howell scheduled to begin teaching?

- Capitalize abbreviations of days and months, parts of addresses, and titles of members of the armed forces. Also capitalize all letters in the abbreviations of states.
  EXAMPLES: Tues.; Nov.; 201 S. Main St.; Maj. Donna C. Plunkett; Boston, MA

D. Circle each letter that should be capitalized. Write the capital letter above it.

1. niles school art fair
   sat., feb. 8th, 9 A.M.
   110 n. elm dr.
2. shoreville water festival
   june 23–24
   mirror lake
   shoreville, mn 55108
3. october fest
   october 28 and 29
   9 A.M.–5 P.M.
   63 maple st.
4. barbara dumont
   150 telson rd.
   markham, ontario L3R 1E5
5. captain c. j. neil
   c/o *ocean star*
   p.o. box 4455
   portsmouth, nh 03801
6. dr. charles b. stevens
   elmwood memorial hospital
   1411 first street
   tucson, az 85062

E. **Write a sentence to show each use of capital letters.**

1. Name of a holiday ______________________________

____

2. Name of a restaurant in your community ______________________________

____

3. Name of a favorite book ______________________________

____

4. Name of an author ______________________________

____

5. Name of a business firm in or near your community ______________________________

____

6. Name of a country ______________________________

____

7. Name of a song ______________________________

____

8. Name of a magazine ______________________________

____

9. A direct quotation ______________________________

____

10. Name of a musician ______________________________

____

11. A title that is written as part of a name ______________________________

____

12. Name of a college or university ______________________________

____

13. Name of a river or lake ______________________________

____

14. Name of an actor or actress ______________________________

____

Using End Punctuation

- Use a **period** at the end of a declarative sentence.
  EXAMPLE: Sunlight is essential for the growth of plants.
- Use a **question mark** at the end of an interrogative sentence.
  EXAMPLE: How much sunlight does a plant need?

A. Use a period or question mark to end each sentence below.

1. Doesn't Sandra's family now live in Missouri___
2. "Snow Time" is a well-known poem___
3. Isn't someone knocking at the door, Beth___
4. Didn't Janice ask us to meet her at 2:30 this afternoon___
5. In Yellowstone Park, we saw Morning Glory Pool, Handkerchief Pool, and Old Faithful___
6. The greatest library in ancient times was in Alexandria, Egypt___
7. Aren't the employees' checks deposited in a different bank___
8. Will Ms. Wilson start interviewing applicants at 10:00 A.M.___
9. My uncle has moved to Calgary, Alberta___
10. Corn, oats, and soybeans are grown in Iowa___
11. Isn't Alex the chairperson of our committee___
12. I've mowed the lawn, pulled the weeds, and raked the leaves___
13. Did the American Revolution begin on April 19, 1775___
14. Is El Salvador in Central America___

B. Add the correct end punctuation where needed in the paragraphs below.

Did you know that experts say dogs have been around for thousands of years___ In fact, they were the first animals to be made domestic___ The ancestors of dogs were hunters___ Wolves are related to domestic dogs___ Like wolves, dogs are social animals and prefer to travel in groups___ This is called pack behavior___

There have been many famous dogs throughout history___ Can you name any of them___ In the eleventh century, one dog, Saur, was named king of Norway___ The actual king was angry because his people had removed him from the throne, so he decided to make them subjects of the dog___ The first dog in space was a Russian dog named Laika___ Laika was aboard for the 1957 journey of *Sputnik*___ Most people have heard of Rin Tin Tin and Lassie___ These dogs became famous in movies and television___

There are several hundred breeds of dogs throughout the world___ The smallest is the Chihuahua___ A Chihuahua weighs less than two pounds___ Can you think of the largest___ A Saint Bernard or a Mastiff can weigh over 150 pounds___

- Use a **period** at the end of an imperative sentence.
  EXAMPLE: Open this jar of tomatoes for me, please.
- Use an **exclamation point** at the end of an exclamatory sentence and after an interjection that shows strong feelings. If a command expresses great excitement, use an exclamation point at the end of the sentence.
  EXAMPLES: Look at the stars! Ouch! I'm so excited!

C. Add periods or exclamation points where needed in these sentences below.

1. Answer the telephone, Michael___
2. Please clean the kitchen for me___
3. Oh___ I can't believe how late it is___
4. Hurry___ The plane is leaving in a few minutes___
5. Carry the bags to the check-in counter___
6. Then run to the waiting area___
7. Hold that seat for me___
8. I can't miss the flight___
9. Stop___ Stop___ You forgot your ticket___
10. Please slow down___
11. Sit down, and put on your seat belt___
12. We're off___
13. Look how small the city is___
14. Please put on your seat belt___
15. Obey the captain's orders___
16. I can't wait until we land___
17. Please give me that magazine___
18. Look___ We're about to land___

D. Add the correct end punctuation where needed in the paragraphs below.

Mr. Henry Modine lives in San Francisco, California___ He often exclaims, "What a wonderful town___" What do you think he does for a living___ Mr. Modine owns a fishing boat, *The Marlin*___ In all of San Francisco, there are few boats as fine as *The Marlin*___ Henry Modine named his boat after the fish his customers like the best – the marlin___ Henry guarantees his customers a fish if they come out on his boat___

"Fantastic___" shouts Henry when someone hooks a marlin___ Henry then says "Bring it in___" Part of Henry's job is to help the fishers reel in the big fish___ Can you believe that some marlins weigh 1,000 pounds or more___ Most of the ones Henry's customers catch weigh about 100 pounds___ They are either striped marlins or black marlins___

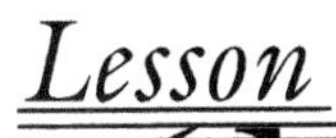

Lesson 61 Using Commas

- Use a **comma** between words or groups of words that are in a series.
  EXAMPLE: Pears, peaches, plums, and figs grow in the southern states.
- Use a comma before a conjunction in a compound sentence.
  EXAMPLE: The farmers planted many crops, and they will work long hours to harvest them.
- Use a comma after a subordinate clause when it begins a sentence.
  EXAMPLE: After we ate dinner, we went to a movie.

A. Add commas where needed in the sentences below.

1. Frank Mary and Patricia are planning a surprise party for their parents.
2. It is their parents' fiftieth wedding anniversary and the children want it to be special.
3. They have invited the people their father used to work with their mother's garden club members and long-time friends of the family.
4. Even though the children are grown and living in their own homes it will be hard to make it a surprise.
5. Mr. and Mrs. Slaughter are active friendly and involved in many things.
6. For the surprise to work everyone will have to be sure not to say anything about their plans for that day.
7. This will be especially hard for the Knudsens but they will do their best.
8. Since every Sunday the families have dinner together the Knudsens will have to become very good actors the week of the party.

- Use a comma to set off a quotation from the rest of a sentence.
  EXAMPLES: "I want to go with you," said Paul.
  Paul said, "I want to go with you."

B. Add commas before or after the quotations below.

1. "We're sorry that we have to cancel our plans" said Earl.
2. Carmen said "But we've done this every week for ten years!"
3. Jeanette said "We have to leave town."
4. Ivan asked "Can't you put it off just one day?"
5. "No I'm afraid we can't" said Earl.
6. "Then we'll just start over the following week" said Carmen cheerfully.
7. Jeanette said "I bet no one else has done this."
8. "I sure hate to spoil our record" said Earl.
9. "Don't worry about it" said Ivan.
10. "Yes everything will work out" said Jeanette.

- Use a comma to set off the name of a person who is being addressed.
  EXAMPLE: Emily, are you ready to go?
- Use a comma to set off words like yes, no, well, and oh at the beginning of a sentence.
  EXAMPLE: Yes, as soon as I find my jacket.
- Use a comma to set off an appositive.
  EXAMPLE: Felix, Emily's dog, is entered in a dog show.

C. Add commas where needed in the sentences below.

1. Anthony a grocery store owner was planning for a busy day.
2. "Diane would you open the store at 9 o'clock?" said Anthony.
3. "Of course that's the time we always open," said Diane.
4. "Pierre the chef at Elaine's will be coming by," he said.
5. Kelly said "Stephanie I'd like some fresh peanuts."
6. "Yes but how many pounds would you like?" answered Stephanie.
7. Ms. Harmon asked "Martin what kind of fresh fruit do you have?"
8. "Well let me check what came in this afternoon," said Martin.
9. Alan the butcher had to wait on fifteen customers.
10. "I don't have time to wait Alan," said Carol.
11. The manager Juan told everyone to be patient.
12. "Please it will go quickly if you all take a number," said Juan.
13. "Yes you're right as usual," said the crowd.
14. Martin the produce manager went behind the counter to help.
15. Well they had sold all of their grapes and tomatoes before noon.
16. "We only have one bushel of green beans left" said Martin.
17. Mr. Loster bought cherries bananas and corn.
18. He was planning a special dinner for Sara his wife.
19. Mr. Loster spent the afternoon cooking baking and cleaning.
20. Today July 18 is her birthday.

D. Add commas where needed in the paragraph below.

Men women boys and girls from across the nation participate in the Special Olympics. Because of this event patterned after the Olympic games boys and girls with disabilities have opportunities to compete in a variety of sports. The Special Olympics includes competition in track swimming and gymnastics. Volunteers plan carefully and they work hard to insure that the event will be challenging rewarding and worthwhile for all the participants. One of my neighbors Chris Bell once worked as a volunteer. "It was an experience that I'll never forget" he said.

Lesson 62 Using Quotation Marks and Apostrophes

- Use **quotation marks** to show the exact words of a speaker. Use a comma or another punctuation mark to separate the quotation from the rest of the sentence. A quotation may be placed at the beginning or at the end of a sentence. Begin the quote with a capital letter.
  EXAMPLES: Pat said, "Please take the dog for a walk." "Please take the dog for a walk," said Pat.
- A quotation may also be divided within the sentence.
  EXAMPLE: "Pat," said Scott, "I just returned from a walk!"

A. Add quotation marks and commas where needed in the sentences below.

1. Wait for me said Laura because I want to go with you.
2. Kim, did you write an article about spacecraft? asked Tom.
3. Where is the manager's desk? inquired the stranger.
4. Joanne asked What is Eric's address?
5. David asked How long did Queen Victoria rule the British Empire?
6. Carlos, did you bring your interesting article? asked the teacher.
7. Good morning said Cindy.
8. Doug asked Did Jim hurt himself when he fell?
9. The meeting begins in ten minutes said Rico.
10. Hoan, you're early said Melissa.
11. Come on, said the coach you'll have to play harder to win this game!
12. Tony said, I know you'll do well in your new job. You're a hard worker.

- Use an **apostrophe** in a contraction to show where a letter or letters have been taken out.
  EXAMPLES: I **can't** remember your name. **I'll** have to think about it.
- Use an apostrophe to form a possessive noun. Add -'s to most singular nouns. Add -' to most plural nouns. Add -'s to a few nouns that have irregular plurals.
  EXAMPLES: **Dina's** house is made of brick. All the **neighbors'** houses are wooden. The **children's** treehouse is wooden.

B. Write the words in which an apostrophe has been left out. Insert apostrophes where they are needed.

1. Kate, didnt you want Sues job? ____________________
2. Havent you seen Pauls apartment? ____________________
3. Jim didnt hurt himself when he fell off Toms ladder. ____________________
4. The employees paychecks didnt arrive on time. ____________________

Lesson 63 Using Colons and Hyphens

- Use a **colon** after the greeting in a business letter.
  EXAMPLES: Dear Mr. Johnson: Dear Sirs:
- Use a colon between the hour and the minute when writing the time.
  EXAMPLES: 1:30 6:15 11:47
- Use a colon to introduce a list.
  EXAMPLE: Our grocery list included the following items: chicken, milk, eggs, and broccoli.

A. Add colons where needed in the sentences below.

1. At 2 1 0 this afternoon, the meeting will start.
2. Please bring the following materials with you pencils, paper, erasers, and a notebook.
3. The meeting should be over by 4 3 0.
4. Those of you on the special committee should bring the following items cups, paper plates, forks, spoons, and napkins.
5. The meeting will deal with the following pool hours, swimming rules, and practice schedules.
6. The lifeguards will meet this evening from 8 0 0 to 1 0 0 0 to discuss responsibilities.
7. We will read the letter at 3 0 0 and have a question-and-answer session.

- Use a **hyphen** between the parts of some compound words.
  EXAMPLES: twenty-one sister-in-law go-getter well-behaved
  air-conditioned middle-aged sixty-six great-grandfather
  blue-green old-fashioned second-story ninety-two
- Use a hyphen to separate the syllables of a word that is carried over from one line to the next.
  EXAMPLE: When the coach has finished his speech, the class mem-
  bers will be allowed to use the pool.

B. Add hyphens where needed in the sentences below.

1. We decided to attend a class on how to use less water when garden
   ing.
2. Our lawn and old fashioned flower gardens need too much water.
3. The sign up sheet at the door was for those who wanted to be on a mailing list.
4. Twenty seven people had already signed up.
5. We saw that our son and daughter in law were there, too.
6. Hank spotted them sitting on an aisle near the center of the audi
   torium.
7. The speaker was a well known expert on gardening.
8. We sat next to our family and learned about long term plans for water conservation.

Review

A. Circle each letter that should be capitalized. Then add the correct end punctuation.

1. mr. j. c. moran owns a car dealership in chicago, illinois___
2. jesse decided to apply for a job on tuesday___
3. wow, mr. moran actually offered him a job___
4. jesse will start work in june___
5. jesse is the newest employee of moran's cars and vans___
6. didn't he get auto experience when he lived in minnesota___
7. he also got training at dunwoody technical institute___
8. jesse took some computer courses there taught by mr. ted woods and ms. jane hart___
9. jesse had only temporary jobs at highland cafe and mayfield electronics for the last two years___
10. since jesse wants to be prepared for his new job, he checked out *automobile technology and the automobile industry* from the windham library___

B. Add commas where needed in the sentences below.

1. After Jesse got the new job his family friends and neighbors gave him a party.
2. Everyone brought food drinks and even some gifts.
3. Bob Jesse's roommate and Carmen Jesse's sister bought him a briefcase.
4. His mother and father bought him a new shirt jacket and tie for his first day on the job.
5. His father congratulated him by saying "Jesse we are happy for you and we wish you the best in your new job."
6. Jesse replied "Well I'm also very excited about it and I want to thank all of you for the party and the gifts."

C. Add commas and quotation marks where needed in the sentences below.

1. How did you get so lucky Jesse? asked Mike.
2. It wasn't luck answered Jesse because I studied before I applied for this job.
3. I didn't know you could study to apply for a job said Mike laughing.
4. Mike I read an employment guide before I applied said Jesse.
5. I have never heard of an employment guide! exclaimed Mike.
6. It's a great book said Jesse.
7. Jesse I'd like to apply for a job at Moran's said Mike.
8. Jesse replied Why don't you read my guide to prepare for the interview?

D. Insert apostrophes, colons, and hyphens where needed in the sentences below.

1. Joe King, Jesses best friend, is the one who gave Jesse the employment guide to use for his interview at Morans.
2. Jesse didnt know important interview skills.
3. The guide offered twenty five helpful hints.
4. The guide suggested the following dress neatly, be on time, be polite, and be enthusiastic.
5. Jesse also used the guides suggestions for preparing a resume listing his work experience.
6. Jesses list contained these items his employers names and addresses, dates of employment, and job descriptions.
7. The guide said Jesse should be a well informed applicant, so he researched salespersons duties and made a list of questions to ask.
8. Jesses guide recommended getting to the interview early to have time to fill out the employers application forms.
9. Jesse arrived at Mr. Morans office at 345 for his 400 interview.
10. The interview lasted forty five minutes, and Jesse was relaxed and self confident when he left.
11. Mr. Morans phone call the next day at 130 let Jesse know he had gotten the job.
12. Jesse needed to do the following pick up a salespersons manual, fill out employment forms, and enroll in the companys insurance program.

E. Punctuate the letter below. Circle each letter that should be capitalized.

73 e. river st.
chicago, il 65067
may 30, 2006

Dear mr. moran,

I just wanted to thank you for offering me the salespersons position with your company___ you mentioned in our interview that my duties would be the following selling cars and vans checking customers credit references and assisting customers with their paperwork___ ive studied the automobile sales guide that you gave me and i feel that im prepared to do a terrific job for morans___ thank you again im looking forward to starting next monday___

sincerely,
jesse sanchez

Using What You've Learned

A. Circle each letter that should be capitalized below. Add punctuation where needed.

720 w. raven
newland, va 27890
may 4, 2006

Dear sirs:

on may 3, 2006, i received the compact disc player i had ordered from your catalog___ the following pieces were missing from the package the battery pack the high quality headphones and the adapter___ please let me know what i should do about this___ will you send the pieces or should I return the whole package___ since your motto is that customers happiness is your goal i thought i would let you know that im not very happy about this___ ive ordered other things in the past___ they were great___ what happened to my order this time___ im waiting anxiously for your answer___

Sincerely yours,
bonita williams

B. Circle each letter that should be capitalized. Add punctuation where needed.

478 n. beacon
trainor, in 73210
june 1, 2006

Dear ms. williams:

please excuse us___ this is awful___ do send the entire package back and we will replace it___ how can we apologize properly___ first, we will send your new compact disc player special delivery so you will get it quickly___ second, we will enclose a copy of *sounds of the nineties* for your pleasure___ we are sorry___ thank you for your past orders___ our customers happiness is our major goal___ well do everything we can to make sure that this order goes through properly___ please let us know if everythings there___ we look forward to hearing from you___

Gratefully yours,
the sound team

C. Rewrite the letter below. Capitalize any letters that should be capitalized. Add needed punctuation.

720 w. raven
newland, va 27890
june 27, 2006

Dear sound team:

hurray___ my compact disc player arrived today and its great___ thank you___ now when I walk my dog i can listen to a CD___ thank you also for *sounds of the nineties*___ can you believe it___ i have a copy of *tunes of the eighties* and had planned to buy *sounds of the nineties*___ now i dont have to___ thats great___

I also want to thank you for your courteous letter___ im sure mistakes can happen to anyone___ everyones quick action was greatly appreciated___ your letter and package arrived at 10 00 this morning___ youre fantastic___

Sincerely,
bonita williams

____
____
____

____

____
____
____
____
____
____
____
____
____
____

____
____

Writing Sentences

- Every sentence has a base consisting of a simple subject and a simple predicate.
  EXAMPLE: Amanda baked.
- Expand the meaning of a sentence by adding adjectives, adverbs, and prepositional phrases to the sentence base.
  EXAMPLE: **My cousin** Amanda baked **a delicious orange cake for dessert.**

A. Expand the meaning of each sentence base by adding adjectives, adverbs, and/or prepositional phrases. Write each expanded sentence below.

1. (Carl swam.)

   ____

2. (Clock ticked.)

   ____

3. (Snow falls.)

   ____

4. (Sun rose.)

   ____

5. (Fireworks exploded.)

   ____

B. Imagine two different scenes for each sentence base below. Write an expanded sentence to describe each scene you imagine.

1. (Students listened.) **a.** ______________________________

   b. ______________________________

2. (Jason wrote.) **a.** ______________________________

   b. ______________________________

3. (Kamal played.) **a.** ______________________________

   b. ______________________________

4. (Juan drove.) **a.** ______________________________

   b. ______________________________

5. (We helped.) **a.** ______________________________

   b. ______________________________

Lesson 65 Writing Topic Sentences

- A **topic sentence** states the main idea of a paragraph. It is often placed at the beginning of a paragraph.

  EXAMPLE:

  Mario was asked to write an article about the new recreation center for the school paper. He wrote a list of questions to ask. He interviewed the park superintendent. He found out about the old park and why it was necessary to build a recreation center.

A. Underline the topic sentence in each paragraph below.

1. Mario knew that having good questions was very important to a successful interview. He thought carefully about what he wanted to know. Then he divided his questions into groups. Some were about the building. Some were about recreation. Others were about the staff.

2. He wanted to include something about the history of the park. He found out who first owned the land. He also asked how people had used the park over the years.

3. Mario found out that the park was nearly as old as the town itself. It had been the scene of picnics, baseball games, carnivals, concerts, and holiday festivals. Political meetings had also been held there.

B. Write a topic sentence for each group of sentences below.

1. **Topic Sentence:** ______________________________

   a. James Leland was the park superintendent.
   b. He had worked in the field of recreation and sports all his adult life.
   c. His father had been a high school teacher and coach.
   d. His grandfather had been a popular baseball player.

2. **Topic Sentence:** ______________________________

   a. Mario enjoyed talking to James.
   b. He found out more than he had ever expected.
   c. James told him why the community needed the center.
   d. The city had grown, and it needed to provide recreation for its residents.

C. Think of a topic you are interested in. Write the topic on the line. Then write a topic sentence.

Topic: ______________________________

Topic Sentence: ______________________________

____

Lesson 66 Writing Supporting Details

- The idea expressed in the topic sentence can be developed with sentences containing **supporting details.** Details can include facts, examples, and reasons.

A. Circle the topic sentence, and underline only the sentences containing supporting details in the paragraph below.

Mario asked Theresa to help him with the article. She would write out the recorded interviews. She would also make suggestions for changes. Theresa is very athletic. Finally, they would both work on typing the article.

B. After each topic sentence, write five sentences containing supporting details.

1. You must be organized when writing an article.

a. ______

b. ______

c. ______

d. ______

e. ______

2. It is important to learn all you can about your topic.

a. ______

b. ______

c. ______

d. ______

e. ______

C. Write four sentences that contain supporting details for the topic sentence you wrote in Exercise C, page 96.

Topic Sentence: ______

a. ______

b. ______

c. ______

d. ______

Ordering Information Within a Paragraph

- One way to organize information in a paragraph is to put it in **chronological order**—the time in which events occurred. Words such as first, next, second, then, finally, and later are used to indicate the order in which events happen. EXAMPLE: **First,** Mario checked his recorder. **Then** he left for the interview.
- Another way to organize information is to use **spatial order.** Words such as above, near, over, beside, right, left, closer, farther, up, and down are used to express spatial relationships. EXAMPLE: The bald eagle sat on **top** of the tree. He watched the pond **below.**

A. Read each paragraph below and tell whether it is in chronological order or spatial order. For the paragraph in chronological order, underline the time order words. For the paragraph in spatial order, underline the words that indicate spatial order.

1. The park board of directors must first approve the architect's design for the recreation center. Then they must develop and approve a budget for the construction of the center. Finally, they can give approval to construction of the center.

   Order: ______________________________

2. The plan for the recreation center includes play areas for young children. A slide and swingset will be built next to a large sand box. A jungle gym will be to the left of the slide. Children will be able to climb to the top of the jungle gym and then jump down to the ground.

   Order: ______________________________

B. Number the details below in chronological order.

_______ Then early in March, the park board of directors approved the architect's design.

_______ Next, the budget was approved in April.

_______ The center's roof was finally completed in August.

_______ In January, the architect first finished his design.

C. Choose one of the scenes below. Write a paragraph of at least four sentences describing the scene. Use spatial order words to show location.

Scenes: your house, a ballpark, a restaurant, a theater, a friend's house

____

____

____

____

Lesson 68 Topic and Audience

- The **topic** of a story or an article is the subject written about.
- The **audience** is the group of readers.
  EXAMPLES: students, family members, neighbors, readers of a newspaper

A. Choose the most likely audience for each topic listed below.

a. first-graders **b.** the city council **c.** high-school students **d.** parents

_______ **1.** Star Athlete Visits Students at Recreation Center

_______ **2.** Study Shows Connection between Time Spent Exercising and Student Progress in School

_______ **3.** Peter Rabbit Here for Hop and Jump Exercises

_______ **4.** Council Considers Tax Plans to Finance Recreation Center

_______ **5.** Tryouts for High School Track Team on Friday

_______ **6.** Study Shows City Budget Shortfall Next Year

_______ **7.** Kelsey School Parents' Night Next Thursday

_______ **8.** Officer Safety to Visit Young Students Next Week

_______ **9.** State University Considers Raising Tuition

_______ **10.** Governor Approves Funds to Expand City Bus Service

B. Read the paragraph below. Then answer the questions that follow.

On Tuesday evening, May 2, 2006, at 6:00, Hawkeye, the mascot of the Child Protection Foundation, will be at the park with his handler, Officer Roy Meyers. While Hawkeye, the long-eared hound, entertains the youngsters, Officer Meyers will discuss the topic "Keeping Your Children Safe." This unusual pair has traveled across the state to introduce the findings on topics such as accidents in the home, hazardous toys, and bike safety.

1. What is the topic of the paragraph?

____

2. Name two possible audiences for the paragraph.

____

3. Explain why each audience might be interested.

Audience 1: ____

Audience 2: ____

C. Choose a topic in which you are interested. Write the name of the topic, and name the audience it would be most likely to interest.

Topic: ____

Audience: ____

Lesson 69 Clustering

■ A **clustering diagram** shows how ideas relate to a particular topic. The topic is written in the center. Related ideas are written around the topic. Lines show the connections between the ideas.

EXAMPLE:

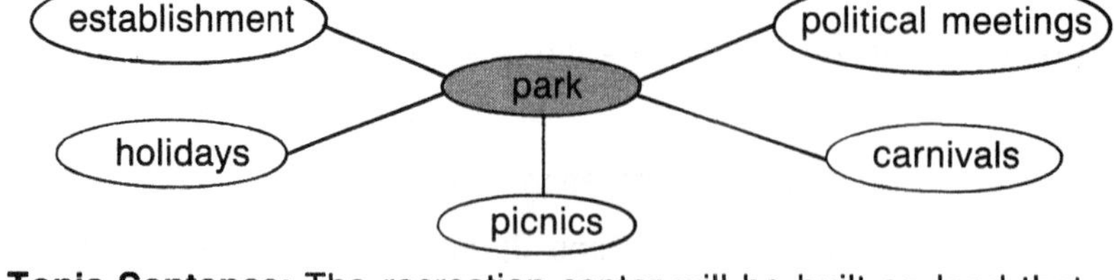

Topic Sentence: The recreation center will be built on land that was once a park.

A. Read each paragraph below. Notice the underlined topic sentence as you read. Then fill in each cluster to show how the details relating to that topic sentence could have been chosen.

1. <u>Mario had a great deal of work to do for the article</u>. He had to finish the interviews, decide what information to use, and write a rough draft. He then had to revise the draft, type the final copy, and proofread it.

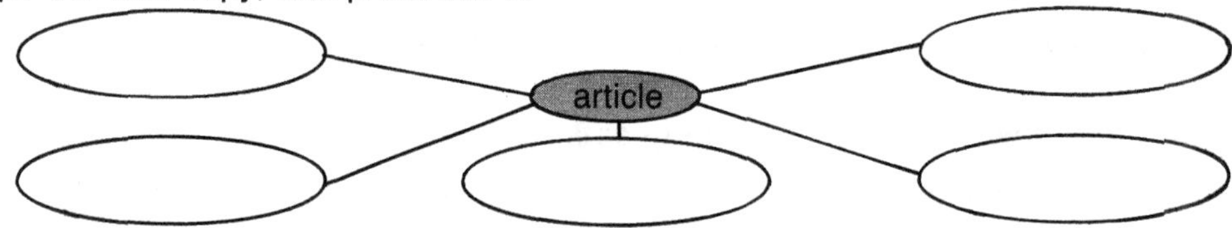

2. <u>Theresa worked hard on the article.</u> She typed the interviews. She edited the article. She organized the rough draft. Finally, she helped with the final revision and proofreading.

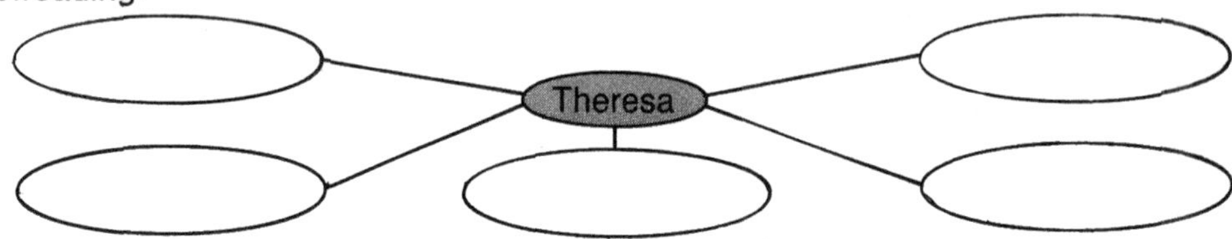

B. Rewrite the topic sentence you wrote on page 93, Exercise C.

Topic Sentence: ______________________________

C. Write that topic from Exercise B in the center of the cluster below. Then fill in the cluster with details that would support your main topic.

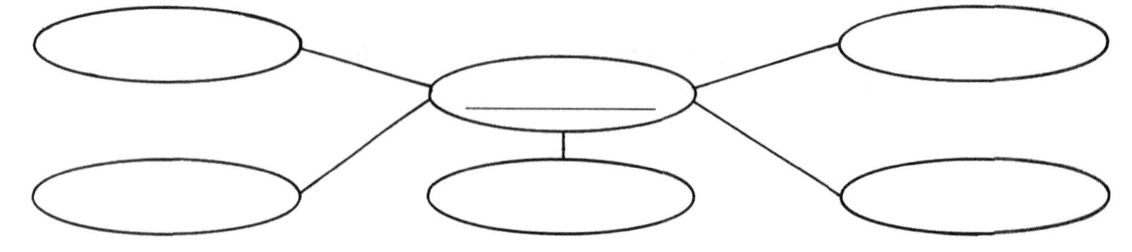

Lesson 70 Outlining

- Before you write about a topic, organize your thoughts by making an **outline.** An outline consists of the title of the topic, **main headings** for the main ideas, and **subheadings** for supporting ideas.
- Main headings are listed after Roman numerals. Subheadings are listed after capital letters.

Topic: The need for a recreation center

I. Problems with park
  A. Age of equipment
  B. Limited usefulness for residents
II. Advantages of recreation center
  A. Wide range of uses
  B. Safe, up-to-date equipment

- **Refer to your topic sentence on page 100, Exercise B. Write an outline based on the clusters, using the example outline as a guide.**

Topic: ______________________

I. ______________________
  A. ______________________
  B. ______________________
II. ______________________
  A. ______________________
  B. ______________________
III. ______________________
  A. ______________________
  B. ______________________
IV. ______________________
  A. ______________________
  B. ______________________
V. ______________________
  A. ______________________
  B. ______________________

Lesson 71 Preparing Interview Questions

- Writers use interviews to get information. Good interview questions will encourage the person being interviewed to talk freely about the subject.
  EXAMPLES: Why do we need a recreation center? Who will be involved in making decisions?
- Avoid questions that can be answered either yes or no by beginning them with words such as who, what, why, and how.
  EXAMPLE: Why do we need a recreation center?

A. Write who, what, when, where, why, or how to complete each question.

1. ________________ will vote on the budget for the recreation center?
2. ________________ will be the various uses of the center?
3. ________________ will the center be paid for?
4. ________________ will the center be located?
5. ________________ do you think a recreation center is necessary?
6. ________________ will the center be completed?

B. Rewrite the questions below so that they cannot be answered yes or no.

1. Does the park have an interesting history?

____

2. Is the location of the park good?

____

3. Does the council have plans to raise local taxes?

____

4. Will the townspeople have a say on the new recreation center?

____

C. Choose a topic and write three questions about it. Remember to begin each question with who, what, when, where, how, or why.

Topic: ____

1. ____
2. ____
3. ____

Writing Based on an Interview

- Many factual articles are based on information gathered in an interview. The writer asks questions about the subject he or she wants to cover and then uses the information to write an article.

- **Read the notes from the interview. Then read the paragraph that Mario and Theresa wrote, and answer the questions that follow.**

Question 1: James, how do you feel about the proposed recreation center?

Answer: It is definitely needed. The park is too small for our growing city and needs massive repairs anyway. It will be good for the whole city to have a well-equipped recreation center.

Question 2: Your family has been involved in sports for many years. How do you feel about the modern approach to physical fitness for people of all ages?

Answer: Physical fitness is vital for everyone. That's why the new recreation center is so important. It will offer facilities and programs for everyone, regardless of age or current fitness levels.

Question 3: What will the recreation center include?

Answer: The center will house an indoor pool, a small ice rink, two gyms, meeting rooms, arts-and-crafts facilities, and locker rooms with showers. We also hope to include a weight-lifting room.

According to Mr. James Leland, park superintendent, the new recreation center will be a welcome addition to the city's facilities. The old park is now outdated and can no longer fill the needs of the people. Mr. Leland recommends that the park be the site of the new recreation center. Its facilities, which will include an indoor pool and two gyms, will fit everyone's needs, regardless of age or current fitness levels.

1. Does the author quote Mr. Leland exactly? ____________________

2. Write one sentence in the article that came from question 1.

____

____

3. Write one sentence in the article that came from question 3.

____

____

4. Write another question that Mario could have asked Mr. Leland.

____

5. What other things will the recreation center include that were not in the article?

____

Lesson 73 Revising and Proofreading

- **Revising** gives you a chance to rethink and review what you have written and to improve your writing. Revise by adding words and information, by taking out unneeded words and information, and by moving words, sentences, and paragraphs around.
- **Proofreading** has to do with checking spelling, punctuation, grammar, and capitalization. Use proofreader's marks to show changes needed in your writing.

Proofreader's Marks

		Take something out.
Capitalize.	Add a period.	Correct spelling.
Make a small letter.	Add quotation marks.	Indent for new paragraph.
Add a comma.	Add something.	Move something.

A. Rewrite the paragraph below. Correct the errors by following the proofreader's marks.

The berryton city council today appruved plans today for construction of a New recreation center mayor june booth said the center to be located on the sight of the currant adams park will provide berryton residents with a variety of recreational programs" the center's facilities include will an indoor pool to gymnasiums arts-and-crafts facilities and a small ice rink and an indoor pool Several meating rooms will also be Included too for use buy various organizations.

B. Read the paragraphs below. Use proofreader's marks to revise and proofread the paragraphs. Then write your revised paragraphs below.

Representatives from severals community organizations attended the meeting to express their support of the recreation center "Construction of this center is Long Overdue Are members will now have a central place in which to meat instead of crowding into each other's homes said Milton Sayre chairman of the berryton citizens senior league

plans call for a groundbreaking ceremony on thursday may 16 at 2 30 followed by a reception in adams park Construction is scheduled mayor booth supervisor john leland and city council members will participate all residents are invited to join them at the ceremoney

Review

A. Expand the sentence bases below by adding adjectives, adverbs, and prepositional phrases.

1. (Friends visited.)

____

2. (Actors prepared.)

____

3. (Window broke.)

____

B. Read the paragraph below. Then circle the topic sentence, and underline only the supporting details.

Phonograph records have changed over the years. Thomas Edison made them from glass, and he used sound waves to carve the grooves into the records. Edison also invented electricity. Later, phonographic records were made of plastic. Today's compact discs are often made with aluminum.

C. Complete the cluster for the topic given in the center.

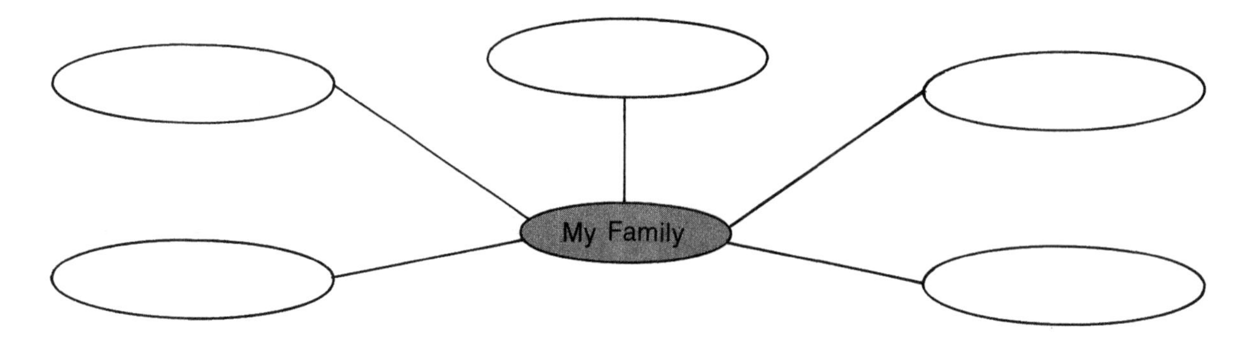

D. Begin an outline based on that cluster.

Topic: My Family

I. ____

A. ____

B. ____

II. ____

A. ____

B. ____

E. Number the following sentences in chronological order. Circle any words that indicate chronological order.

_______ Finally, put your ear close to the victim's mouth to be sure that air is coming out of the lungs.

_______ Next, pinch the victim's nostrils together.

_______ Begin by tilting the person's head so that his or her chin points upward.

_______ Then take a deep breath, and breathe into the mouth of the victim.

F. Rewrite the interview questions below so that they cannot be answered yes or no.

1. Do you think we need a high-speed train for mass transit in the city?

____

2. Do you agree that the train should run through town?

____

3. Will the citizens have any input into the final route?

____

4. Does the city council have plans to finance the train?

____

G. Read the paragraph that was written from the interview above. Then answer the questions that follow.

According to Council member Adelia Rodriguez, the city of Centerville needs to build a new high-speed train to serve its citizens in the future. This train would follow a north-south route through the most populated areas of town. The final route would be determined by a panel of experts hired by the city planning commission.

1. Write a sentence that came from interview question 3. ____

____

2. Which question was not answered in the article? ____

H. Rewrite the paragraph below. Correct the errors by following the proofreader's marks.

¶once the fog cleared James drove the to the airport to pick up his Sister. When he got their, he discorved the plane was late he asked the ticket person, When will the flight from mexico city arrive the person told him it would be another two hours.

____

____

____

____

Using What You've Learned

Choose a topic in which you are interested.

____

B. Decide who your audience will be.

____

C. Write a topic sentence.

____

D. Draw a cluster diagram for your topic. Draw more circles for supporting details if necessary.

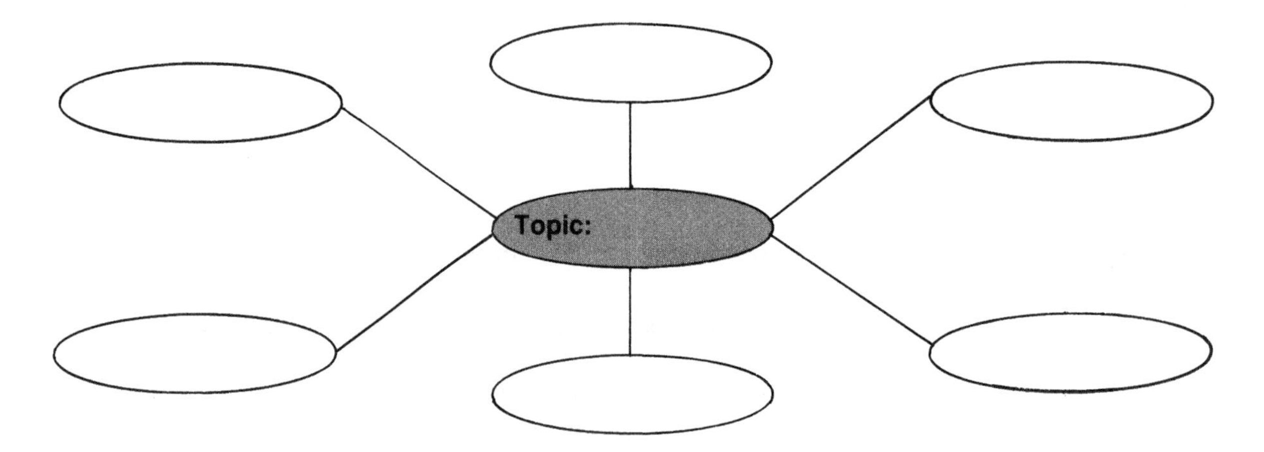

E. Write a short outline for a report on your topic.

I. ______________________________

A. ______________________________

B. ______________________________

II. ______________________________

A. ______________________________

B. ______________________________

III. ______________________________

A. ______________________________

B. ______________________________

F. **Write five questions about your topic that you would ask if you had an interview with someone who is an expert on the subject.**

1. ______________________________

2. ______________________________

3. ______________________________

4. ______________________________

5. ______________________________

G. **Write a paragraph with a topic sentence and at least five sentences containing supporting details. Then revise and proofread your paragraph.**

____

____

____

____

____

____

____

H. **Rewrite the paragraph below. Correct the errors by following the proofreader's marks. Use the proofreader's marks on page 104 if necessary.**

¶ One of the most importantest peaces of fire savety equipment is the smoke detector The smoke detector continually all the time monitors the air in you're house. it sounds an alarm at the first sign of trouble Fire officials consider the smoke detectors won of the most best effective low-cost devices alarms available Today.

____

____

____

____

____

____

____

____

Lesson 74 Dictionary: Guide Words

- A **dictionary** is a reference book that contains definitions of words and other information about their history and use.
- **Entries** in a dictionary are listed in **alphabetical order.**
- **Guide words** appear at the top of each dictionary page. Guide words show the first and last entry on the page.

  EXAMPLE: The word lease would appear on a dictionary page with the guide words learn / lesson. The word lever would not.

A. Put a check in front of each word that would be listed on a dictionary page with the given guide words.

1. fade / flat

_______ faster
_______ face
_______ flavor
_______ fetch
_______ flatter
_______ factory
_______ flag
_______ fancy
_______ flop
_______ fertile
_______ flow
_______ flame

2. image / inform

_______ information
_______ impossible
_______ insect
_______ incomplete
_______ ignore
_______ immense
_______ indeed
_______ improve
_______ insist
_______ infect
_______ imagine
_______ inherit

3. radio / reach

_______ rail
_______ rabbit
_______ ranch
_______ real
_______ raw
_______ raccoon
_______ raft
_______ read
_______ ramp
_______ rate
_______ reduce
_______ rake

B. Number the words in each column in the order of their appearance in a dictionary. Then write the words that could be the guide words for each column.

1. ____________ / ____________

_______ bedroom
_______ blend
_______ blame
_______ biography
_______ block
_______ blink
_______ bear
_______ benefit
_______ believe
_______ beach

2. ____________ / ____________

_______ dine
_______ depend
_______ determine
_______ department
_______ district
_______ disease
_______ disturb
_______ discard
_______ difference
_______ dessert

3. ____________ / ____________

_______ fire
_______ face
_______ free
_______ finger
_______ faint
_______ flower
_______ family
_______ follow
_______ fair
_______ flavor

Lesson 75 Dictionary: Syllables

- A **syllable** is a part of a word that is pronounced at one time. Dictionary entry words are divided into syllables to show how they can be divided at the end of a writing line.
- A **hyphen** (-) is placed between syllables to separate them.
  EXAMPLE: quar-ter-back
- If a word has a beginning or ending syllable of only one letter, do not divide it so that one letter stands alone.
  EXAMPLES: a-fraid bus-y

A. Find each word in a dictionary. Then write each word with a hyphen between each syllable.

1. allowance ____________
2. porridge ____________
3. harness ____________
4. peddle ____________
5. character ____________
6. hickory ____________
7. solution ____________
8. variety ____________
9. talent ____________
10. weather ____________
11. brilliant ____________
12. enthusiasm ____________
13. dramatic ____________
14. employment ____________
15. laboratory ____________
16. judgment ____________
17. kingdom ____________
18. recognize ____________
19. usual ____________
20. yesterday ____________

B. Write two ways in which each word may be divided at the end of a writing line.

1. victorious vic-torious victori-ous
2. inferior ____________ ____________
3. quantity ____________ ____________
4. satisfactory ____________ ____________
5. security ____________ ____________
6. possession ____________ ____________
7. thermometer ____________ ____________
8. getaway ____________ ____________

Dictionary: Pronunciation

- Each dictionary entry word is followed by a respelling that shows how the word is **pronounced.**
- An **accent mark** follows a syllable that is said with extra stress. In some words more than one syllable is stressed. The syllable that receives primary stress is followed by a **primary accent mark (′).** The syllable that receives secondary stress is followed by a **secondary accent mark (′).**
  EXAMPLE: sub-sti-tute (sub′ stə tūt′)
- A **pronunciation key** (shown below) explains the other symbols used in the respellings.

A. Use the pronunciation key to answer the questions.

1. How many words are given for the symbol ə? ________
2. What symbol is used for the sound of the s in treasure? ________
3. What symbol would be used for the sound of a in bar? ________
4. What symbol would be used for the sound of wh in whether? ________
5. What symbol would be used for the sound of a in around? ________
6. What symbol would be used for the sound of oo in hoot? ________

at; **ā**pe; f**ä**r; c**â**re; **e**nd; m**ē**; **i**t; **ī**ce; p**î**erce; h**o**t; **ō**ld; s**ô**ng; f**ô**rk; **oi**l; **ou**t; **u**p; **ū**se; r**ü**le; p**u̇**ll; t**û**rn; **ch**in; si**ng**; **sh**op; **th**in; **th**is; **hw** in **wh**ite; **zh** in trea**s**ure. The symbol **ə** stands for the unstressed vowel sound in **a**bout, tak**e**n, penc**i**l, lem**o**n, and circ**u**s.

B. Use the pronunciation key to help you choose the correct word for each respelling. Underline the correct word.

1.	(hēl)	hail	heel	hole
2.	(ī′ vē)	ivy	I've	eve
3.	(thā)	thee	they	the
4.	(let′ ər)	letter	lighter	litter
5.	(kāp)	cap	cop	cape
6.	(ri tīr′)	retort	retire	writer
7.	(ri trēt′)	retreat	retread	retrial
8.	(sap)	soap	sip	sap
9.	(doun)	den	down	dawn
10.	(nū)	no	now	new
11.	(hīt)	hit	height	hate
12.	(noiz)	nosy	nose	noise
13.	(wāt)	what	wit	weight
14.	(dī′ mənd)	diamond	demand	depend
15.	(ī′ ərn)	horn	earn	iron
16.	(lēd)	loud	lead	load

Lesson 77 Dictionary: Definitions and Parts of Speech

- A dictionary lists the **definitions** of each entry word. Many words have more than one definition. In this case, the most commonly used definition is given first. Sometimes a definition is followed by a sentence showing a use of the entry word.
- A dictionary also gives the **part of speech** for each entry word. An abbreviation (shown below) stands for each part of speech. Some words may be used as more than one part of speech.

  EXAMPLE: **mess** (mes) *n.* **1.** an untidy, usually dirty, condition.
  -*v.* to make untidy and dirty.

- **Use the dictionary samples below to answer the questions.**

cage (kāj) *n.* a structure in which animals can be kept. *v.* to lock up or keep in a cage.

cos-tume (kos′ to͞om) *n.* **1.** an outfit worn in pretending to be someone else: *Karla's costume was the nicest one in the play.* **2.** a type of dress associated with a particular people, place or time. -*v.* to provide with a costume.

cot-ton (kot′ ən) *n.* **1.** soft fibers that grow in a cluster on seed pods of certain plants and are used to make cloth. **2.** the plant on which these fibers grow. **3.** thread made from cotton fibers. **4.** cloth woven of cotton. -*adj.* made of cotton: *The cotton dress might shrink in warm water.*

n.	noun
pron.	pronoun
v.	verb
adj.	adjective
adv.	adverb
prep.	preposition

1. Which words can be used as either a noun or a verb? ______________________

2. Which word can be used as an adjective?

   ____

3. Which word has the most meanings?

   ____

4. Which word can be used as a noun or as an adjective? ______________________

5. Write the most commonly used definition of costume. ______________________

   ____

6. Write a sentence in which you use cage as a verb. ______________________

   ____

7. Write a sentence using the first definition of costume. ______________________

   ____

8. Use the second definition of cotton in a sentence. ______________________

   ____

Dictionary: Word Origins

- An **etymology** tells of an entry word's origin and development. Many dictionary entries include an etymology.
- The etymology is usually enclosed in brackets [ ] after the definition of the entry word. The language from which the entry word came into English is listed first, followed by the language from which that word came, and so on. Often the symbol < is used to save space and stands for the phrase "is derived from" or "comes from."

  EXAMPLE: **tu-lip** (to͞o' lip, tyo͞o' lip) [Lat. *Tulipa* < Turk. *tülibend,* turban < Pers. *dulband.*] The word *tulip* came into English from the New Latin word *Tulipa,* which came from the Turkish word *tülibend,* which meant "turban." The word *tülibend* came from the Persian word *dulband.*

- **Use the dictionary samples below to answer the questions.**

e-mo-tion (i mō' shən) *n.* strong feeling. [Middle French *emouvoir* to stir up, from Latin *exmovēre* to move away, disturb from *ex* + *movēre* to move.]

gup-py (gup' ē) *n.* a small, brightly-colored freshwater fish. [After R. J. L. Guppy (1836–1916), who introduced the fish to England.]

line (līn) *n.* a long, narrow mark as with pen or pencil. [A combination of Old French *ligne* string, cord and Old English *line* cord, rope.]

load (lōd) *n.* **1.** that which is put on a pack animal to carry. **2.** cargo put on a ship, plane, train, or truck. [Middle English *lod,* from Old English *lād* support, carrying.]

mar-a-thon (mar' a thon') *n.* a cross-country foot race. [After *Marathon,* Greece (so called because in 490 B.C. a messenger ran from Marathon to Athens to announce a victory over the Persians).]

1. Which word comes from the name of a person? __________
2. Which word originally meant "to move"? __________
3. Which languages are in the history of the word line? __________
4. Which word comes from both Middle English and Old English? __________
5. Which word comes from the name of a place? __________
6. Which words have more than one language in their histories? __________
7. What is the meaning of the Latin word exmovēre? __________
8. Why is the guppy named after R. J. L. Guppy? __________
9. What did the Middle English word lod come from? __________
10. Why do we call a long race a marathon? __________
11. Which word comes from a word that meant "support or carrying"? __________
12. Which word comes from the word ligne? __________
13. Which words come from French? __________

Lesson 79 Using Parts of a Book

- A **title page** lists the name of a book and its author.
- A **copyright page** tells who published the book, where it was published, and when it was published.
- A **table of contents** lists the chapter or unit titles and the page numbers on which they begin. It is at the front of a book.
- An **index** gives a detailed list of the topics in a book and the page numbers on which each topic is found. It is in the back of a book.

A. Answer the questions below.

1. Where should you look for the page number of a particular topic? ______
2. Where should you look to find out who wrote a book? ______
3. Where should you look to get a general idea of the contents of a book? ______
4. Where should you look to find out when a book was published? ______
5. Where should you look to find the name of the book? ______
6. Where should you look to find out who published a book? ______

B. Use your *Language Exercises* book to answer the questions.

1. What company published this book? ______
2. How many units are in this book? ______
3. On what page does Unit 2 start? ______
4. Where is the index located? ______
5. What is the copyright date? ______
6. What pages contain lessons on pronouns? ______
7. On what page does Unit 5 start? ______
8. On what pages are the lessons on commas found? ______
9. What lesson is on page 86? ______
10. List the pages that teach prepositions. ______
11. On what page is the lesson on guide words found? ______
12. On what page is the lesson on prefixes found? ______
13. On what page does Unit 3 start? ______

Lesson 80 Using Visual Aids

- A **chart** lists information in columns, which you read down, and rows, which you read across. The information can be either words or numbers.
- A **graph** shows how quantities change over time. It often shows how two or more things change in relation to one another. The information can be shown through the use of lines, dots, bars, pictures, or in a circle.

A. Use the chart and the graph to answer the following questions.

Library Use Chart

Day of the Week	Science Students	History Students
Monday	18	5
Tuesday	22	16
Wednesday	14	10
Thursday	4	20
Friday	13	15

Library Use Graph

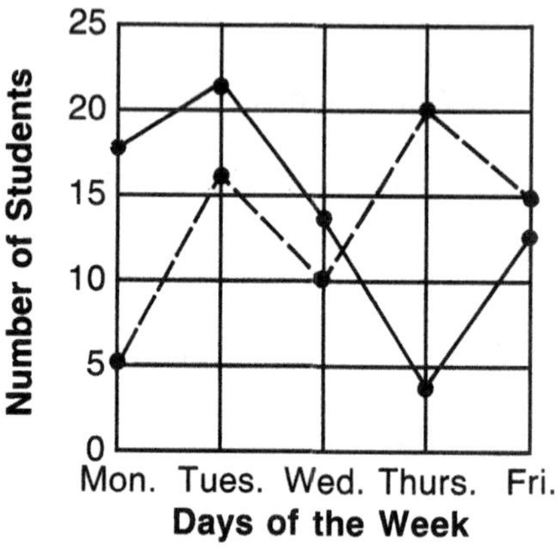

Graph Key
Science students _____
History students _ _ _

1. How many science students used the library on Monday? __________ on Tuesday? __________

   on Wednesday? __________ on Thursday? __________ on Friday? __________

2. Can the question in number 1 be answered by studying the Library Use Chart? __________

   the Library Use Graph? __________

3. On which day was the number of science and history students using the library

   nearly the same? __________

4. On which day did the most science and history students use the library? __________

5. How many science and history students used the library on the day

   mentioned in number 4? __________

6. On which day did the least number of science and history students use the library? __________

- A **road map** is another valuable type of visual aid. Maps like the one shown below are helpful when you are unfamiliar with a certain area. To use any map, you should refer to its **legend, compass rose,** and **scale.**
- The legend tells what each symbol represents.
- The compass rose is made up of arrows that point north, south, east, and west.
- The scale allows you to determine how far it is from one location to another. To use the scale, mark the distance between any two locations along the edge of a sheet of paper. Then place the sheet of paper alongside the scale of distance, lining up one of the marks with zero. This will allow you to read the distance between the two locations.

B. Use the map to answer the questions below.

Carsonville

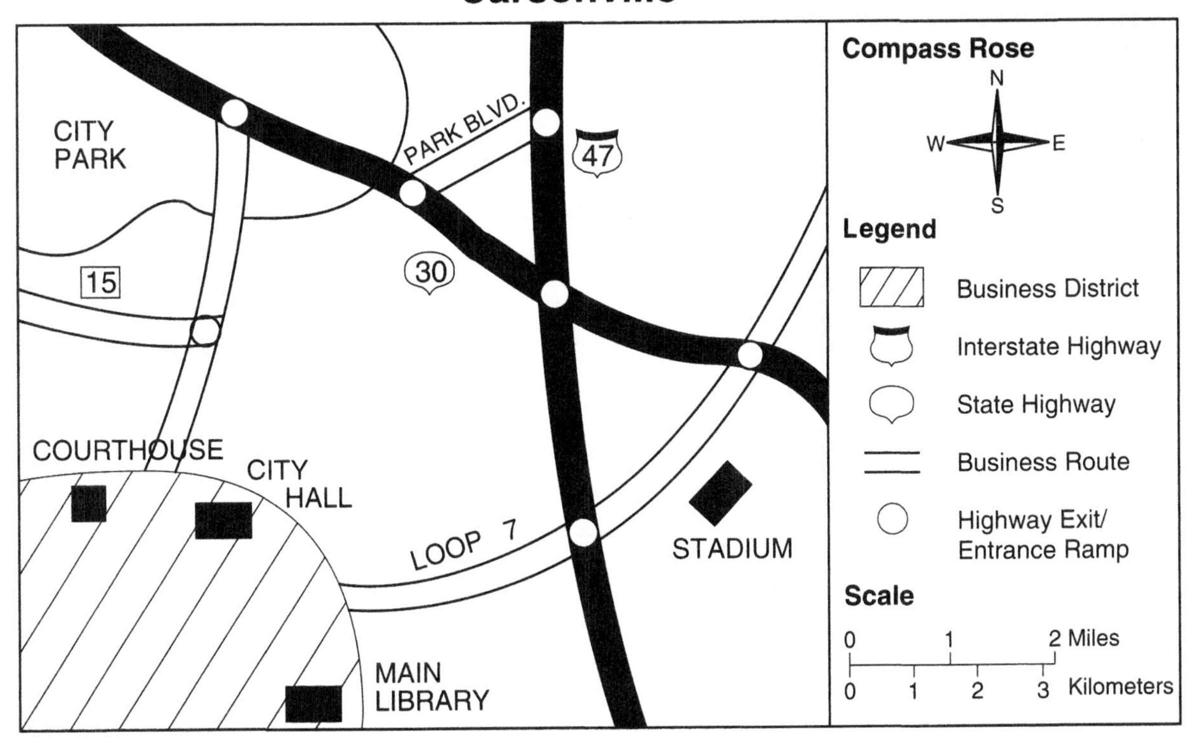

1. Which direction from the business district is City Park? ____________________
2. On what road is the stadium? ____________________
3. How many miles is it from City Hall to the Main Library? ____________________
4. What kind of highway is 30? ____________________
5. Does Business Route 15 run north/south or east/west? ____________________
6. Is the Courthouse within the business district? ____________________
7. How many exit ramps are there on Highway 30 from Loop 7 to City Park? ____________________
8. How many miles will you travel if you drive from City Park to the stadium? ____________________

Lesson 81 Using the Library

■ Books are arranged on library shelves according to **call numbers**. Each book is assigned a number from 000 to 999, according to its subject matter. The following are the main subject groups for call numbers.

000–099	Reference	500–599	Science and Mathematics
100–199	Philosophy	600–699	Technology
200–299	Religion	700–799	The Arts
300–399	Social Sciences	800–899	Literature
400–499	Languages	900–999	History and Geography

A. Write the call number group in which you would find each book.

1. *2006 World Almanac and Book of Facts* ____________________
2. *Mathematics for Today* ____________________
3. *Global Warming: A World Problem* ____________________
4. *Philosophy Through the Ages* ____________________
5. *Spanish: A Romance Language* ____________________
6. *Technology Takes Over* ____________________
7. *Splitting the Atom* ____________________
8. *The Encyclopedia of Mammals* ____________________
9. *The Impressionist School of Painting* ____________________
10. *Children's Stories from Around the World* ____________________
11. *The Study of Forgotten Societies* ____________________
12. *The New Russia* ____________________
13. *The Religions of the World* ____________________
14. *The Reader's Guide* ____________________
15. *Dance in North America* ____________________

B. Write the titles of three of your favorite books. Write the call number range beside each title.

1. ____________________
2. ____________________
3. ____________________

Lesson 82 Using a Card Catalog

- The **card catalog** contains information cards on every book in the library. Some libraries are now computerized and have no card catalogs, but the information in the computer is filed in the same manner as the information in the card catalog.
- Each book has three cards in the catalog. The cards are filed separately according to: 1. the author's last name, 2. the subject of the book, and 3. the title of the book.
- Most smaller libraries use the **Dewey Decimal System** to organize their books. Each book is assigned a **call number** from 000 to 999, according to its subject matter.

A. Refer to the sample catalog card to answer the questions about one book.

Subject Card

Call number	363.73 **Air Pollution**	Subject
Author	**Baines, John D.**	
Title	Conserving the atmosphere: an introduction to the problems confronting the earth's atmosphere, and what can be done to stop its destruction. Austin Texas,	Place published
Publisher	Raintree/Steck-Vaughn (1989)	Date published
Number of pages	48 p. illus.	Illustrated

1. What is the title? ______________________________
2. Who is the author? ______________________________
3. Who published it? ____________________ When was it published? ____________________
4. What is the call number? ____________________ How many pages does it have? ____________________
5. What is the general subject? ______________________________
6. Does it contain illustrations? ______________________________

B. Write author, title, or subject to tell which card you would look for to locate the book or books.

1. books about mountain climbing ____________________
2. *Life in the Chinese Countryside* ____________________
3. a book of short stories by O. Henry ____________________
4. a book by Jane Austen ____________________

Lesson 83 Using an Encyclopedia

- An **encyclopedia** is a reference book that contains articles on many different topics. The articles are arranged alphabetically in volumes. Each volume is marked to show which articles are inside.
- Guide words are used to show the first topic on each page.
- At the end of most articles there is a listing of **cross-references** to related topics for the reader to investigate.

A. Find the entry for Knute Rockne in an encyclopedia. Then answer the following questions.

1. What encyclopedia did you use? ______________________
2. When did Knute Rockne live? ______________________
3. Where was he born? ______________________
4. Where did he go to college? ______________________
5. For what is he best known? ______________________

B. Find the entry for Redwood in an encyclopedia. Then answer the following questions.

1. What encyclopedia did you use? ______________________
2. Where does the redwood tree grow? ______________________
3. By what other name is it known? ______________________
4. What is special about this tree? ______________________
5. How tall do most redwoods grow? ______________________

C. Find the entry in an encyclopedia for a person in whom you are interested. Then answer the following questions.

1. Who is your subject? ______________________
2. What encyclopedia did you use? ______________________
3. When did the person live? ______________________
4. Where did the person live? ______________________
5. What is it about the person that makes him or her famous? ______________________

   ____
6. What cross-references are listed? ______________________

Lesson 84 Using an Encyclopedia Index

- Most encyclopedias have an **index** of subject titles, listed in alphabetical order. The index shows the volume and the page number where an article can be found. Some encyclopedias contain articles on many different topics. Other encyclopedias contain different articles relating to a broad general topic.

- **Use the sample encyclopedia index to answer the questions below.**

Index

Acorn Squash, **1**–6; **11**–1759
  Baked, supreme, **1**–7
  Steamed, **1**–7
Appetizer(s), **1**–841; *see also* Cocktail; Dip; Pickle and Relish; Spread
  Almonds, **1**–89
  Celery, stuffed, **1**–89
  Cheese Ball, **3**–429
Cabbage, **2**–256; *see also* Salads, Coleslaw; Sauerkraut
  with bacon and cheese sauce, **1**–68
Flour, **5**–705
  Peanut, **8**–1328
  Rice, **10**–1556
  Wheat, **12**–1935

1. In what volume would you find an article on stuffed celery? __________

2. On what page would you find information on cabbage with bacon and cheese sauce? __________

3. Are all articles on flour found in the same volume? __________

4. What are the cross-references for **Appetizers**? __________

5. Do the words in bold show the name of the volume or the name of the main food or ingredient? __________

6. Which main food or ingredient has articles in two volumes? __________

7. Information on which appetizers can be found in the same volume and on the same page? __________

8. What main ingredient is found in Volume 5? __________

9. If you looked under **Dip**, what might you expect to find as a cross-reference? __________

10. Information on what appetizer would be found in Volume 3? __________

11. Information on what ingredient is found on page 1328 in the encyclopedia? __________

Lesson 85 Using a Thesaurus

- A **thesaurus** is a reference book that writers use to find the exact words they need. Like a dictionary, a thesaurus lists its entry words alphabetically. Each entry word has a list of **synonyms *(syn.)*,** or words that can be used in its place. Some thesauruses also include **antonyms *(ant.)*** for each entry word.

  EXAMPLE: You have just written the following sentence: I was so hungry that I **ate** my lunch quickly. With the help of a thesaurus you could improve your sentence by replacing ate with a more specific synonym, such as devoured. I was so hungry that I **devoured** my lunch quickly.

A. Refer to the sample thesaurus entry below to answer the questions.

difficult *adj.* ***syn.*** puzzling, complex, awkward ***ant.*** simple, effortless

1. Which is the entry word? ____________________
2. What are its synonyms? ____________________
3. Which word would you use to describe something complicated? ____________________
4. Which word would you use to describe something baffling? ____________________
5. Which word would you use to describe something that might be embarrassing? ____________________
6. What are the antonyms of difficult? ____________________
7. Which antonym would you use to describe a test that is easy? ____________________

B. Use one of the synonyms of difficult to complete each sentence.

1. As an engineer, Marie designs very ____________________ pieces of machinery.
2. We found ourselves in a very ____________________ situation when we arrived too early.
3. Manuel is very good at solving ____________________ mysteries.

C. Write three sentences, each containing a different synonym of difficult.

1. ____________________
____
2. ____________________
____
3. ____________________
____

D. Study the thesaurus entry for talk. Then use a synonym of talk to complete each sentence.

> **talk** *v. syn.* mention, chat, discuss, whisper, argue, describe, grumble, say

1. Out of courtesy to others, you should always ______________________ in a movie theater.
2. Please ______________________ your house so that I can find it easily.
3. If you must ______________________, you should try not to lose your temper.
4. My sister often likes to ______________________ with her college buddies.
5. Can we ______________________ the new proposal sometime?
6. You always know the right thing to______________________.
7. My younger brothers always ______________________ when they're tired and cranky.
8. Did I ______________________ that I will be gone tomorrow?

E. Write five sentences, each containing a different synonym of talk.

1. ____
2. ____
3. ____
4. ____
5. ____

F. Circle the synonym that best completes each sentence.

1. The batter (looked, glared) at the umpire after his bad call.
2. The (noise, roar) of the crowd was deafening.
3. My brother (aged, matured) after he graduated from high school.
4. My friends often (accumulate, gather) at the park.
5. The man used a (knife, blade) to cut the freshly baked bread.
6. It is my (judgment, opinion) that we all need a vacation now and then.
7. I felt a (loop, knot) in my stomach as I walked up the aisle.
8. I can almost (imagine, think) what it would be like to fly.
9. I (knocked, pushed) the vase over, and water spilled on the floor.
10. I was reading when the tornado (alarm, bell) sounded.
11. I (floated, drifted) to sleep while reading last night.
12. I will miss our cottage after we (leave, abandon) it for the year.
13. We (disguised, hid) our friend's present in her closet.

Lesson 86 Using the *Readers' Guide*

- The ***Readers' Guide to Periodical Literature*** lists by author and by subject all the articles that appear in nearly two hundred magazines. Use the *Readers' Guide* when you need
  - Recent articles on a particular subject,
  - Several articles written over a period of time about the same subject,
  - Many articles written by the same author.

- **Use the *Readers' Guide* samples to answer the questions.**

Subject Entry

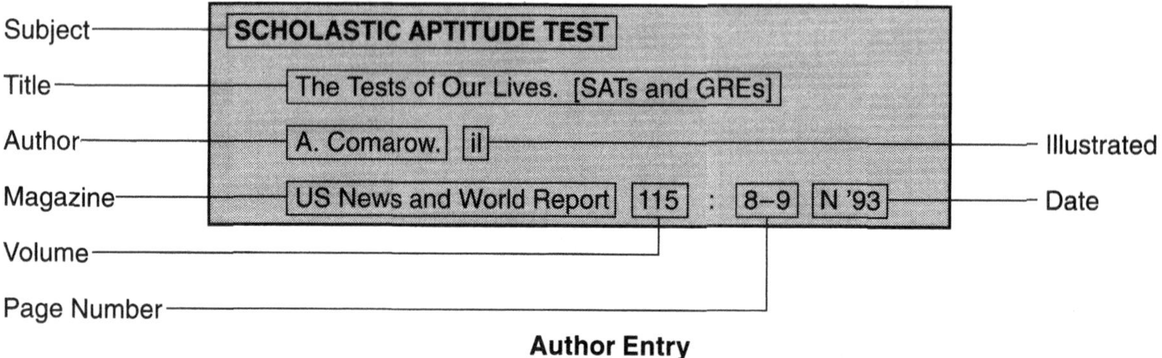

Author Entry

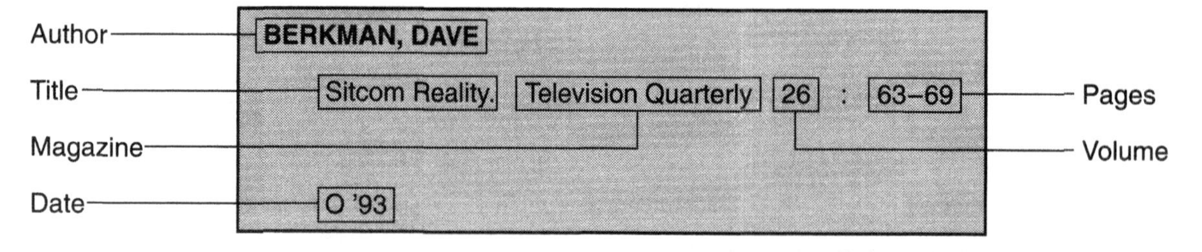

1. Who wrote the article "Sitcom Reality"? ____________________
2. In what magazine will you find the article "The Tests of Our Lives"? ____________________
3. Who is the author of "The Tests of Our Lives"? ____________________
4. In what magazine will you find the article "Sitcom Reality"? ____________________
5. Under what subject entry might you find the article "Sitcom Reality"? ____________________
6. On what pages will you find the article "Sitcom Reality"? ____________________
7. In what volume of US News & World Report does "The Tests of Our Lives" appear? ____________________
8. In what month and year was "The Tests of Our Lives" published? ____________________
9. What abbreviation is used for the word illustrated? ____________________
10. In what month and year was "Sitcom Reality" published? ____________________

Lesson 87 Choosing Reference Sources

- Use a **dictionary** to find the definitions of words and pronunciations of words, suggestions for word usage, and etymologies.
- Use an **encyclopedia** to find articles about many different people, places, and other subjects. Use an encyclopedia to find references to related subjects.
- Use a **thesaurus** to find synonyms and antonyms.
- Use the ***Readers' Guide to Periodical Literature*** to find magazine articles on specific subjects or by particular authors.
- Use an **atlas** to find maps and other information about geographical locations.
- Use an **almanac,** an annual publication, to find such information as population numbers, annual rainfall, election statistics, and other specific information for a given year.

- **Write dictionary, encyclopedia, thesaurus, *Readers' Guide,* atlas, or almanac to show where you would find the following information. Some information may be found in more than one source.**

_______________ 1. the life of Queen Elizabeth I

_______________ 2. an article on the last space shuttle flight

_______________ 3. the states and provinces through which the Rocky Mountains run

_______________ 4. the origin of the word tomato

_______________ 5. the annual rainfall for Somalia

_______________ 6. the most direct route from California to Alberta

_______________ 7. an antonym for the word happy

_______________ 8. the meaning of the word spar

_______________ 9. recent articles written on the subject of air pollution

_______________ 10. the pronunciation of the word wren

_______________ 11. the life of Sigmund Freud

_______________ 12. a synonym for the word bad

_______________ 13. the years during which World War I was fought

_______________ 14. an article on rock climbing

_______________ 15. the final standings of the National Football League for last year

_______________ 16. the meaning of the word history

Using Reference Sources

- Use reference sources—dictionaries, encyclopedias, the *Readers' Guide to Periodical Literature,* thesauruses, atlases, and almanacs—to find information about people, places, or things with which you are not familiar. You can also use these sources to find out more about subjects that interest you.

A. Follow the directions below.

1. Choose a person from history that you would like to know more about.

   Person's name: ______________________________

2. Name two reference sources that you can use to find information about this person.

   a. ______________________________

   b. ______________________________

3. Use one of the reference sources you named above. Find the entry for the person you are researching. Write the exact title of the reference.

   ____

4. Write a short summary of the information you found.

   ____

   ____

   ____

   ____

5. Name the source that would contain recent articles about this person.

   ____

6. Look up your person's name in the reference source you listed in number 5. Write the titles of three articles that were listed.

   a. ______________________________

   b. ______________________________

   c. ______________________________

7. Which articles above, if any, can be found in your library?

   ____

8. Name a subject heading under which you might find more information on your person.

   ____

B. Follow the directions, and answer the questions.

1. Choose a country you would like to know more about.

   Name of country: ______________________

2. List four reference sources that you can use to find information about this country.

   a. ______________________ c. ______________________

   b. ______________________ d. ______________________

3. Find the entry for the country in one of the reference sources you listed. Write the exact title of the reference source.

   ____

4. Write a short summary of the information you found.

   ____

   ____

   ____

   ____

   ____

5. Find the entry for the country in one other reference source. Write the exact title of the reference source.

   ____

6. What new information did you find about the country?

   ____

   ____

   ____

C. Follow the directions, and answer the questions below.

1. In what state do you live? ______________________
2. Find the entry for your state in one of the reference sources. Write the exact

   title of the reference source. ______________________

3. Write a short summary of the information you found about your state.

   ____

   ____

   ____

   ____

Review

A. Use the dictionary samples below to answer the questions.

ex-pose (eks pōz′) *v.* **1.** to leave open to external influence: *He was exposed to the measles.* **2.** to make known. **3.** to permit light to reach, as in photography. [Middle English *exposen,* from Middle French *exposer,* from Latin *exponere* to set forth, explain.]
ex-po-si-tion (eks pə zish′ ən) *n.* **1.** a large public display. **2.** the act of explaining ideas or facts.
ex-press (eks pres′) *v.* **1.** to put into words: *Tom always wants to express his views.* **2.** to show outwardly: *Her face expressed sadness.* **3.** to send something quickly: *They expressed the package overnight.* [Middle English, from Middle French *expres,* from Latin *expressus* to press out, express.]
ex-qui-site (eks kwiz′ it) *adj.* **1.** of great beauty: *The exquisite sculpture was put on display.* **2.** of extremely high quality. *The exquisite necklace was one of a kind.* [Middle English, from Latin *exquisitus* from *exquirere* to search out, from *ex* + *quaerere* to seek.]

1. Underline the words that could be guide words for the dictionary page above.
   - a. expel / expire
   - b. expand / expense
   - c. export / extend
   - d. extra / extreme
2. What part of speech is expose? ____________ exposition? ____________ express? ____________
3. How many syllables does the word exposition have? ____________ express? ____________
4. Write the correct word for each respelling.
   - a. (eks kwiz′ it) ____________
   - b. (eks pōz′) ____________
   - c. (eks pə zish′ ən) ____________
   - d. (eks pres′) ____________
5. What word comes from the Latin word expressus? ____________
6. From what three languages does the word expose come?

   ____________ ____________ ____________
7. Write one sentence in which you use express according to its second definition.

   ____
8. What word comes from a Latin word that means "to search out"? ____________

B. Write title page, copyright page, table of contents, or index to tell where to find this information.

____________ 1. the author's name

____________ 2. the chapter titles

____________ 3. the year the book was published

____________ 4. the page number on which a particular topic can be found

____________ 5. the publisher's name

____________ 6. the book's title

C. Use the map to answer the questions.

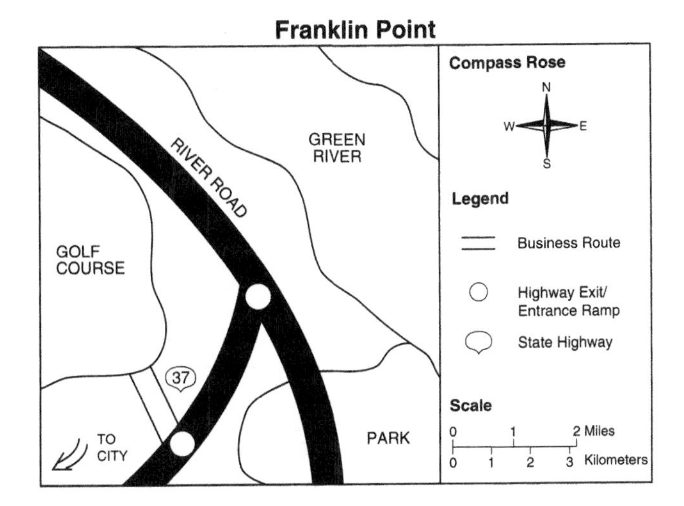

1. Which direction is the city from the park? ______

2. What kind of highway is 37? ______

3. How far is it from the exit on River Road to the golf course? ______

D. Use the sample thesaurus entry below to answer the questions.

activity *n.* ***syn.*** action, movement, motion ***ant.*** inactivity, inaction, motionlessness

1. What is the entry word? ______

2. What are its antonyms? ______

E. Use the *Readers' Guide* sample to answer the questions.

KAGARLITSKY, BORIS
Make Them Truly Democratic. The Nation 257:688–702 Dec '93

1. What is the title of the article? ______

2. In what magazine does the article appear? ______

3. On what pages will you find the article? ______

F. Write dictionary, encyclopedia, thesaurus, *Readers' Guide*, atlas, or almanac to show where you would find the following information.

1. the most direct route from Calgary, Alberta, to Albuquerque, New Mexico ______

2. the pronunciation of the word sedentary ______

3. an antonym for the word bright ______

4. the life of John James Audubon ______

5. the increase in world population last year ______

Using What You've Learned

A. Find the word humor in your dictionary. Then follow the directions and answer the questions.

1. Write the guide words from the page on which you found the entry for humor. ____________

2. Write humor in syllables. ____________

3. As what parts of speech can humor be used? ____________

4. Write the history of the word. ____________

____

B. Use the sample catalog card to answer the questions.

> 520.0
>
> **Lambert, David**
> Stars and planets: includes information on the planets, the solar system, astronomy, and astronautics in astronomy.
> Austin, Texas, Colonial Press [1994] 32 p. illus.

1. What type of catalog card is this?

   a. subject card **b.** author card **c.** title card

2. What is the call number of the book? ____________

3. What is the title of the book? ____________

4. Is the book illustrated? ____________

C. Use the encyclopedia sample to answer the questions.

> **CREE** is the name of a Native American people now living on reservations in Canada. They were originally forest hunters and trappers who traded with the early French and English fur traders. Part of the group moved southwest into buffalo country and became known as Plaines Cree. *See also* NATIVE AMERICANS.

1. What is the article about? ____________

2. Where did some members of the tribe move? ____________

3. Under what subject heading can you find related information?

____

D. Use the *Readers' Guide* sample to answer the questions.

> **HERTSGAARD, MARK**
> Onward and Upward with the Arts: Letting It Be.
> il New Yorker 69: Jan 24, '94

1. What is the title of the article? ______________________________

2. Who is the author? ______________________________

3. In what magazine does the article appear? ______________________________

E. Use a thesaurus to find a synonym for each underlined word.

______________ 1. My milk shake was so <u>large</u> that I couldn't finish it.

______________ 2. The police <u>found</u> our stolen property.

F. Use the information in the chart to complete the graph. Then answer the questions.

Club Membership

Chart

Year	Men	Women
1960	40	40
1970	30	10
1980	20	30
1990	30	30

Graph

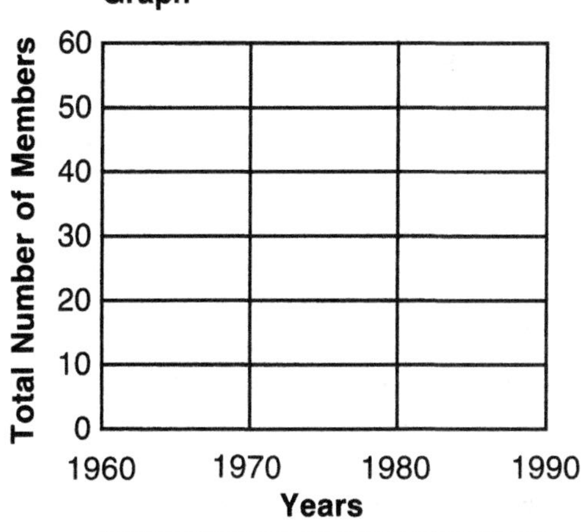

1. How many women belonged to the club in 1960? ______________________________

2. What was the total number of members in 1960? ______________________________

3. What two years had an equal number of members? ______________________________

G. Use the sample encyclopedia index entry to answer the questions.

> **Generation(s), 5**-877; *See also* Families; Grandparents

1. In what volume is the article on generations? ______________________________

2. On what page does the article begin? ______________________________

Final Review

Synonyms and Antonyms ▪ On the line before each pair of words, write S if they are synonyms, or A if they are antonyms.

_______ **1.** brave, courageous

_______ **2.** start, commence

_______ **3.** happy, unhappy

_______ **4.** late, early

_______ **5.** smile, grin

_______ **6.** quick, slow

_______ **7.** begin, end

_______ **8.** country, nation

_______ **9.** sweet, sour

Homonyms ▪ Underline the correct homonyms in each sentence below.

1. Tina went (by, buy)(plain, plane) to visit her (ant, aunt).

2. We had a (great, grate) tour of the (capital, capitol) building.

3. The kitten had white (hair, hare), large (pause, paws), and a long (tail, tale).

Homographs ▪ Circle the letter for the best definition for each underlined homograph.

1. Lee ate the rest of the meatball sandwich.

a. part left over **b.** inactive period of time

2. The heat in the desert was unbearable.

a. to abandon **b.** dry, barren land

3. John's club had a car wash to raise money for their trip.

a. a heavy wooden stick **b.** an organization of people

4. The room is light because it has many windows.

a. bright **b.** not heavy

5. Please tear the article out of the magazine for me.

a. a drop of water from the eye **b.** rip

Prefixes, Suffixes, and Compound Words ▪ Write P if the underlined word has a prefix, write S if it has a suffix, and write C if it is a compound word.

1. _______ _______ Tony was careful as he walked uphill to the soggy field.

2. _______ _______ It seemed awfully wet for the softball game. He was not hopeful.

3. _______ _______ He began to rethink his decision to play. Perhaps he had been foolish.

4. _______ _______ His teammates would be helpless in this mud.

5. _______ _______ The other team felt unhappy. They said running could be hazardous.

6. _______ _______ Suddenly there was a downpour. They would be unable to play.

7. _______ _______ They decided to reschedule the game for the next Thursday afternoon.

8. _______ _______ Tony's team was thankful for the delay. They needed the weekend for extra practice.

9. _______ _______ The game is an important one for everyone. Neither team's pitcher has lost a game yet.

Contractions ▪ Write the contraction for each pair of words.

1. I am ______
2. would not ______
3. do not ______
4. I have ______
5. you have ______
6. is not ______
7. will not ______
8. does not ______
9. I will ______
10. they are ______
11. had not ______
12. there is ______

Connotation and Denotation ▪ For each underlined word, write (-) for a negative connotation, (+) for a positive connotation, or (N) for a neutral connotation.

______ 1. Jake told us a story at the party.

______ 2. Jake is such a showoff.

______ 3. He brags about his sense of humor.

______ 4. Often he tells a hilarious story.

______ 5. This story was dull.

______ 6. In fact, I got bored, so I left.

______ 7. I went home and fell asleep.

______ 8. I slept peacefully all night.

______ 9. Sue giggled at the joke.

______ 10. She wept at the last act.

______ 11. Suddenly he snarled.

______ 12. The curtain came down.

______ 13. We plodded home.

______ 14. We ate delicious muffins.

Idioms ▪ Underline the idiom in each sentence. Then write the meaning of the idiom on the line.

1. The band's new song didn't knock my socks off.

______

2. I was out like a light the moment my head hit the pillow.

______

3. He flew off the handle when he learned his car had been stolen.

______

4. Her smile lit up the sky.

______

5. Makoto let the cat out of the bag when he mentioned the surprise party.

______

6. She was down in the dumps after she missed the speech.

______

7. The good news from his sister put him on cloud nine.

______

8. She was on the fence about the invitation.

______

Final Review Unit 2

Types of Sentences ▪ Before each sentence, write D for declarative, IN for interrogative, IM for imperative, and E for exclamatory. Write X if it is not a sentence. Punctuate each sentence correctly.

1. ______ Oh, the road is closed___
2. ______ What should we do now___
3. ______ Stop talking and let me think___
4. ______ We must find a new road___
5. ______ Need to turn around___
6. ______ I'll pull over to the side of the road___
7. ______ Get the map that's on the backseat___
8. ______ I can find an alternate route___

Subjects and Predicates ▪ Draw a line between the complete subject and the complete predicate in each sentence below. Write SS for a simple subject, CS for a compound subject, SP for a simple predicate, and CP for a compound predicate.

______ ______ 1. Steve washed and waxed his car.

______ ______ 2. Steve's sister and brother helped him polish the chrome.

______ ______ 3. The sky-blue car shone in the sun.

______ ______ 4. Steve keeps his car in good condition.

______ ______ 5. Steve and his neighbor work on the car every weekend.

______ ______ 6. Both young men are taking an auto mechanics course and practice on Steve's car.

______ ______ 7. The car looks great and runs beautifully.

______ ______ 8. Steve and his neighbor both love that car.

Compound Sentences ▪ Combine each pair of sentences below to form a compound sentence.

1. Jason wasn't sure what to do. Maria wasn't helping with her suggestions.

____

2. He listened to what Susan said. Her ideas just wouldn't work.

____

3. It was getting dark. They needed to leave soon.

____

4. Jason had an idea. Maria agreed with the idea.

____

Direct Objects and Indirect Objects ▪ Underline the verb in each sentence. Then write DO above the direct object and IO above the indirect object.

1. The store gave the contest winner a free trip.
2. The coach bought his soccer team pepperoni pizzas.
3. Tomás handed the taxi driver a generous tip.

Correcting Run-on Sentences and Expanding Sentences ▪ Correct the run-on sentence. Then expand each new sentence by adding details.

Lee ran down the track, he was in the lead.

____

____

Independent and Subordinate Clauses ▪ Underline the independent clause, and circle the subordinate clause in each sentence below. Describe the subordinate clause by writing adjective clause or adverb clause on the line before each sentence.

_______________ **1.** The paintings we saw at the museum were beautiful.

_______________ **2.** Before Maria went to college, she traveled for a year.

_______________ **3.** Employees who work the night shift at the plant receive extra pay.

_______________ 4. Marla found her missing keys when she was searching for her briefcase.

_______________ **5.** The landlord remodeled our apartment after we signed the new lease.

_______________ **6.** Edgar Allan Poe was a famous poet who wrote poems and short stories.

_______________ **7.** The dresser we saw at the garage sale was a valuable antique.

_______________ **8.** Carlos volunteered at the community center because he liked helping children.

_______________ **9.** We stopped delivery of the newspaper and the mail since we were going away for a month.

Complex Sentences ▪ Insert the subordinate clause in parentheses into the independent clause to form a complex sentence. Write the complex sentence on the line.

1. (who specializes in cancer research) The doctor spoke to the medical students.

____

2. (when he arrives at his destination) Mr. Burris will notify the office.

____

3. (where we do our research) The library is closed for repairs all week.

____

4. (which has been closed for safety reasons) The coal mine will begin operating again next month.

____

Final Review

Parts of Speech ▪ Write the part of speech above each underlined word. Use the abbreviations given in the box.

n.	noun
pron.	pronoun
v.	verb
adj.	adjective
adv.	adverb
prep.	preposition
conj.	conjunction

1. We had grilled steak, baked potatoes, and a fresh tossed salad for dinner.
2. The exhausted hikers quickly set up their tents and went to sleep.
3. The Japanese gardener pruned the young fruit trees and rose bushes carefully.
4. Anthony tried very hard to finish the mystery novel, but he fell asleep.
5. The island's tourists quietly watched the glorious sunset until it disappeared.

Verbs ▪ Underline the correct verb, and circle the verbal in each sentence.

1. Gardening (is, are) Mr. and Mrs. Butala's favorite hobby.
2. Dean (received, will receive) his swimming medal tomorrow.
3. We (driven, drove) to the lake to fish for trout.
4. The pitcher (has tried, have tried) to throw the runner out.
5. Roberto (chose, chosen) to wait in line for a ticket.
6. The thief (broken, broke) into the office to steal equipment.
7. Mary (have decided, has decided) to move to a new town.
8. The dried spices (smells, smell) wonderful.

Pronouns ▪ Underline the pronoun in parentheses that agrees with the antecedent in each sentence. Circle each antecedent.

1. Scott's brothers gave him (their, his) suggestions.
2. The children took care of the wounded bird and then set (them, it) free.
3. The coach was interviewed by reporters after (his, their) game.

Adjectives and Adverbs ▪ Complete each sentence with the proper form of the adjective or adverb in parentheses.

1. (early) We arrived at the party ______________________ than the other guests.
2. (expensive) The groceries for the cookout were ______________________ than the ones for the birthday party.
3. (tall) Is Luis the ______________________ player on the basketball team?
4. (fresh) Use this loaf of bread for the sandwiches since it is ______________________ than mine.

Grammar and Usage ▪ Fill in the blanks by supplying the word or words specified in parentheses.

Manatees ______________ (linking verb) mammals whose population is endangered. Also known as sea cows, manatees have dark gray skin, a very small head, poorly developed eyes that ______________ (contraction of do) see ______________ (adverb), and two front flippers. ______________ (possessive pronoun) tails are large, rounded flippers. Manatees live ______________ (preposition) shallow, fresh water or saltwater and eat underwater plants. They ______________ (intransitive verb) in the southeastern part ______________ (preposition) the United States, western Africa, South America, the Amazon, and the Caribbean Sea.

Manatees are ______________ (adverb) gentle animals. ______________ (gerund of rub) muzzles is how they communicate. If alarmed, ______________ (subject pronoun) make a ______________ (present participle of chirp) noise. By adulthood, they grow to between eight and fifteen feet ______________ (conjunction) weigh ______________ (adverb) 1,500 pounds. Scientists studying ______________ (limiting adjective) adult manatee ______________ (helping verb) observed that it can eat about 100 pounds of plants in one day.

Manatees ______________ (helping verb) clean waterways by eating vegetation before it blocks narrow passages. In some areas, manatees are encouraged ______________ (infinitive of thrive), so they ______________ (future tense of keep) waterways free of plants. Boats and boat propellers are the ______________ (superlative adjective) enemy of the manatee. In a few places, people hunt ______________ (object pronoun) for meat, oil, and hides. ______________ (demonstrative adjective) hunting has led to the decline of the manatee population. ______________ (conjunction), in most areas, manatees ______________ (protect in passive voice) by law.

Final Review Unit 4

Capitalization and End Punctuation ▪ Circle each letter that should be capitalized. Write the capital letter above it. Add correct end punctuation to each sentence.

1. the road rally will start on nov. 1 in detroit, michigan___
2. tom asked, "how many italian sports cars will be entered___"
3. dr. smith plans to enter betsy, his antique ford___
4. "wow, betsy is the best american car in the rally!" said mr. lane___
5. they heard there might be a special entry from japan___
6. tom asked, "are you sure the entry arrived before the deadline on monday___"
7. mr. lane said, "no, but i did see an address from kyoto, japan, with the list of competitors___"
8. "betsy will have no trouble beating the competition," said tom___

Commas ▪ Add commas where needed in the sentences below.

1. Yes we have visited Japan France and Italy.
2. After we picked up Pepe my poodle from the groomer we took him to the veterinarian.
3. Well I think the judge showed compassion integrity and fairness in the courtroom.
4. Bill the rehearsal is beginning and we need you to join us now.
5. Belinda my oldest sister earns extra money by running errands sewing and cooking for our neighbor.
6. Jeff please finish your report and I will type it for you.

Quotation Marks and Commas ▪ Add quotation marks and commas where needed in the sentences below.

1. Tony said Meg I saw your dog in Kevin's yard.
2. Julio the telegram is for you called his brother.
3. Mr. Simpson asked What time does the softball game begin?
4. Ms. Ito asked the reporter are you going to run for mayor?
5. Our company is on McNeil Road replied the receptionist.
6. You need to improve your defense said Coach Díaz if you expect to win the big game.

Apostrophes ■ **Insert apostrophes where they are needed in the sentences below.**

1. I cant find the consultants report anywhere.
2. The teams new uniforms werent sewn properly.
3. Doesnt that store sell womens jewelry?
4. The horses owner wouldnt sell them for any price.
5. Cant you pick up Stephanies car for her at the repair shop?

Colons and Hyphens ■ **Add colons and hyphens where they are needed in the sentences below.**

1. Our meeting is at 130 this afternoon, and you need to remind the fol lowing people Jim Brown, Patricia West, Ann Tyler, and Jeff Ray.
2. My brother in law helped us move into our second story apartment.
3. Between 100 and 500 yesterday, twenty five people signed the sign up sheet for the conference.
4. That well known Italian restaurant specializes in the following foods lasagna, grilled shrimp, veal, and spaghetti with meatballs.
5. My great grandfather will be eighty seven years old tomorrow.

Punctuation and Capitalization ■ **Circle each letter that should be capitalized below. Add commas, question marks, quotation marks, apostrophes, periods, colons, and hyphens where needed.**

3720 w. anderson
phoenix, az 37825
may 7, 2006

ms. jean jackson
735 w. 79th street
detroit, mi 14728

Dear ms. jackson

i want to enter my antique ford betsy in the Rally of the Americas to be held august 12, 2006___ please send me any information i may need to register___ i understand you only accept seventy five entries___ am i too late___ i was told to wait until may to inquire so i hope there are still openings___

a friend who has entered in the past said this is the best rally of the whole year___ im excited about entering___ my car is a 1910 classic in excellent condition___ it has won numerous awards over the years and it is not ready to retire___ my wife and i are looking forward to the drive from our home in arizona all the way to detroit___ were studying the book *the motor city* in anticipation of our visit___ ill be waiting to hear from you___

Sincerely yours,
dr. lee smith

Composition ■ Read the paragraphs. Then answer the questions that follow.

In order to prove that shipwrecked sailors could survive in an open boat at sea, Dr. Bombard decided to conduct an experiment. First, he chose a 15-foot open rubber boat. Then he decided not to take any food or water with him. Since most shipwrecked sailors die from lack of food or water, he wanted to find a way to survive strictly off the sea. Finally, on October 19, 1953, Dr. Bombard started his journey across the Atlantic Ocean.

Dr. Bombard discovered two very important things on his journey. The most important was that sailors could drink seawater. This was something that many felt would speed death instead of helping people to live. Dr. Bombard drank over a pint of seawater every day and lived to tell about it. His next important discovery was that he could keep from getting diseases caused by lack of proper vitamins by eating plankton. Plankton are small, vitamin-rich plants and animals that float in the sea. Many sea creatures live on plankton. Eating just a teaspoon or so of plankton a day gave him all the vitamins and minerals he needed. He also ate raw fish that he caught daily. Although he lost 56 pounds, Dr. Bombard proved that sailors could survive by living off the sea.

1. Underline the topic sentence in each paragraph.

2. How many supporting details are in the first paragraph? _______ in the second? _______

3. Is the first paragraph written in chronological order or spatial order? ____________________

4. Write the time order words found in the first paragraph.

____________________ ____________________ ____________________

5. What is the topic of the selection? ____________________

6. Write one possible audience that might be interested in the selection.

____

7. Complete the outline for the selection.

I. Dr. Bombard gets ready

A. ____________________

B. ____________________

II. Discoveries

A. ____________________

B. ____________________

8. Write two questions you would ask Dr. Bombard in an interview.

a. ____________________

b. ____________________

Clustering ▪ Read the paragraph. Underline the topic sentence. Then fill in the cluster to show how the details relating to that topic sentence could have been chosen.

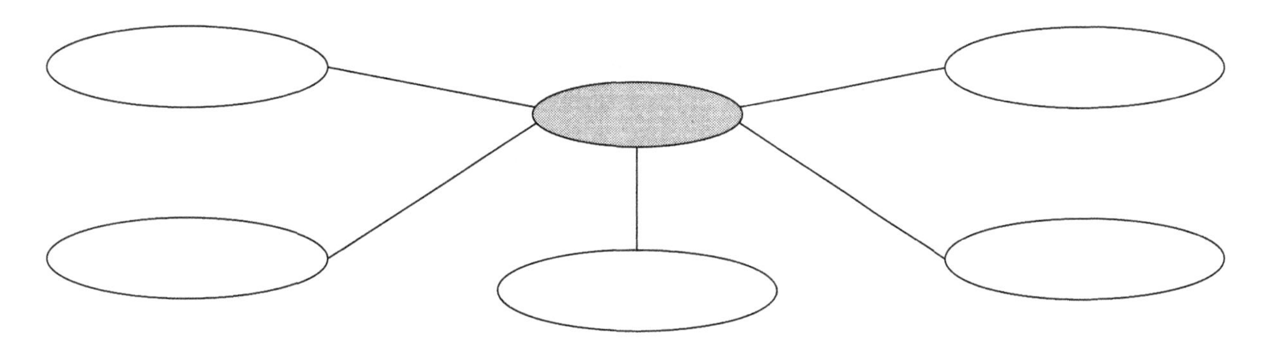

The birth of the island of Surtsey was a violent event. First, a large, black cloud burst from the water. A rumbling sound came from under the ocean. The cloud grew to 12,000 feet high. Giant explosions spewed ash, dust, and hot rocks. A mountain rose from the water. A volcano in the ocean had erupted.

Revising and Proofreading ▪ Read the paragraphs below. Use proofreader's marks to revise and proofread the paragraphs. Then write your revised paragraphs.

Years ago there were Thousands of merry go rounds in the united states Many were made in new york. the carosel horses were hand painted and carved Each horse was difrent. now there are only a few hundred carousels left.

the history of Carousels began in france. solders played a game on horseback Carousels were invented to help the practice for the game

Final Review Unit 6

Using the Dictionary ▪ Use the dictionary samples to answer the questions.

earn (ûrn) *v.* **1.** to receive in return for work done. **2.** To become deserving or worthy; *Nancy earned first place in the tournament.* [Middle English *ernen,* from Old English *earnian*]

earth (ûrth) *n.* **1.** The third planet from the sun. **2.** The dry land of the planet. **3.** Soft, loose, dirt suitable for planting. [Middle English *erthe,* from Old English *eorthe,* related to Old High German *erda,* earth, from Greek *eraze* to the ground]

1. Circle the letter of the guide words for the above entry.

a. east / ebb **b.** each / easily **c.** each / eagle

2. How many definitions are listed for earn? ______ earth? ______

3. Write one sentence using the second definition of earth.

____

4. Write the most commonly used definition of earn. ______________________________

____

5. What part of speech is earn? __________ earth? __________

6. How many syllables do earn and earth have? ______

7. Write the respelling of earn. __________ earth. __________

8. Which word came from the Old English word earnian? ______________________

9. Which word means the same in Old High German as it does in modern English? ____________

Parts of a Book ▪ Write title page, copyright page, table of contents, or index to tell where you would find this information.

____________________ **1.** The page on which specific information can be found

____________________ **2.** The author's name

____________________ **3.** The page on which a chapter begins

____________________ **4.** The year the book was published

Reference Sources ▪ Write D for dictionary, E for encyclopedia, TH for thesaurus, AL for almanac, AT for atlas, or RG for *Readers' Guide* to tell where you would find this information.

______ **1.** an article on the Toronto Blue Jays

______ **2.** the etymology of the word baseball

______ **3.** the history of the Red Cross

______ **4.** the distance between Rome and Naples

______ **5.** a synonym for the word build

______ **6.** planning a vegetable garden

Using Visual Aids ▪ **Use the map to answer the questions.**

1. What direction is the museum from the police station?

 ____

2. How far is it from the museum to the recreation center?

 ____

3. Does First Street run north/south or east/west?

 ____

Poplar Point

POLICE
DAISY DRIVE
81
440
COURTHOUSE
RECREATION CENTER
FIRST STREET
To Park
MUSEUM
Compass Rose
N
W
E
S
Legend
Interstate Highway
State Highway
Business District
Business Route
Highway Exit/ Entrance Ramp
Scale
0 1 2 Miles
0 1 2 3 Kilometers

Using the Library and Card Catalog ▪ **Use the sample catalog card to answer the questions.**

Author Card

643.8
T 620

Tambo, Frank L.
Advances in computer technology—New York:
Macmillan, 1993 271 p.

1. Who is the author? ______________________________

2. What is the book's call number? ______________________________

3. Who is the book's publisher? ______________________________

Using a Thesaurus ▪ **Use the sample thesaurus entry to answer the questions.**

produce *v.* ***syn.*** bear, yield, give, cause, make ***ant.*** waste, destroy

1. What is the entry word? ______________________________

2. What part of speech is produce? ______________________________

3. What are its synonyms? ______________________________

Using the *Readers' Guide* ▪ **Use the *Readers' Guide* sample to answer the questions.**

ICEBERGS
Icehunters. [International Ice Patrol; cover story] M. Dane. il map
Popular Mechanics, 170:76–79 Oct '93

1. Who is the author of this article? ______________________________

2. On what pages is the article? ______________________________

3. Is the article illustrated? ______________________________

Check What You've Learned

A. Write S before each pair of synonyms, A before each pair of antonyms, and H before each pair of homonyms.

_______ 1. mean, cruel _______ 3. terrible, wonderful

_______ 2. bread, bred _______ 4. sore, soar

B. Write the homograph for the pair of meanings.

_______________ 1. to shake 2. a glass container

C. Write P before each word with a prefix, S before each word with a suffix, and C before each compound word.

_______ 1. thoughtful _______ 3. unconventional

_______ 2. handlebar _______ 4. undercover

D. Write the words that make up each contraction.

_______________ _______________ 1. I'd _______________ _______________ 2. don't

E. Underline the word in parentheses that has the more negative connotation.

The concert was (unpleasant, horrible).

F. Circle the number of the idiom that means undecided.

1. up in the air 2. off the wall

G. Write D before the declarative sentence, IM before the imperative sentence, E before the exclamatory sentence, and IN before the interrogative sentence. Then underline the simple subject, and circle the simple predicate in each sentence.

_______ 1. Hey, that isn't yours! _______ 3. I am watching the evening news.

_______ 2. Read me the next question. _______ 4. Who wanted the tuna sandwich?

H. Write CS before the sentence that has a compound subject and CP before the sentence that has a compound predicate.

_______ 1. Kiwis and mangoes are unusual fruits.

_______ 2. The ocean waves pounded and sprayed the beach.

I. Write CS before the compound sentence. Write RO before the run-on sentence. Write I before the sentence that is in inverted order.

_______ 1. Bart loves to swim, and he teaches children's swimming classes.

_______ 2. On the board the next assignment she wrote.

_______ 3. It was over in an instant, no one saw what had happened.

J. Put brackets around the subordinate clause, and underline the independent clause in this complex sentence. Then write DO above the direct object.

Dana gave her the box of chocolates that someone had sent.

K. Underline the common nouns, and circle the proper nouns in the sentence.

It was up to Dr. Martinez to decide how serious Sharise's illness was.

L. Circle the appositive in the sentence. Underline the noun it identifies or explains.

Phoebe, Diane's old-fashioned china doll, is forty-one years old.

M. Write past, present, or future to show the tense of each underlined verb.

________________ 1. He told us that we must act now.

________________ 2. How will we ever get there on time?

________________ 3. She says that her recipe is the best.

N. Circle the correct verbs in each sentence.

1. He (don't, doesn't) care who (drew, drawn) the map.
2. The leaves had (fallen, fell) before she was (gave, given) the rake.
3. He (taken, took) the letter she had (wrote, written).
4. The bell (ring, rang) just as we had (chosen, chose) our seats.

O. Circle the number of the sentence that is in the active voice.

1. The mail arrived later than usual.
2. The announcement was received after the wedding.

P. Write SP before the sentence that has a subject pronoun, OP before the sentence that has an object pronoun, PP before the sentence that has a possessive pronoun, and IP before the sentence that has an indefinite pronoun. Circle the pronoun in each sentence.

______ 1. They found an old diary in a trunk.

______ 2. The author dedicated the new book to him.

______ 3. His father had served in the armed forces for twenty years.

______ 4. Nobody knows what the truth is.

Q. Underline the pronoun. Circle its antecedent.

Robert behaved in his usual quiet manner.

R. On the line before each sentence, write adjective or adverb to describe the underlined word.

________________ 1. Paul is shorter than Greg.

________________ 2. The young woman sat quietly and watched.

________________ 3. I promised to meet her in an hour.

________________ 4. She yelled louder than the others.

S. Underline each prepositional phrase twice. Circle each preposition. Underline the conjunction once.

He sat in a cafe across the street, although she had urged him to join them at the restaurant.

T. Rewrite the letter. Add capital letters and punctuation where needed.

482 w. franklin st.
overhill mt 80897
aug 22 2006

dear ms muller

i received the application you sent me but these enclosures were not included the aptitude test the self addressed envelope and the postcard___ would you please send them as soon as possible___ i want to complete everything just as you want it___

id like to confirm our appointment for wednesday september 14 at 315 P.M. i look forward to seeing you then and talking with you about the scholarship___

yours truly
roy thompson

____

____

____

____

____

____

____

____

____

____

U. Number the sentences in order, with the topic sentence first.

_______ **1.** Then the logs are taken by truck to a pulp mill.

_______ **2.** The bark is cut off, and the logs are made into pulp.

_______ **3.** Finally, the pulp is heated and dried.

_______ **4.** First, trees are cut down.

_______ **5.** Look at how paper is made.

V. Circle the number of the best interview question.

1. What are the main objections to the expansion project?

2. Does your organization have any other alternatives?

W. Rewrite the sentence below. Correct the errors in the sentence by following the proofreader's marks.

pluto is not only smalest planet the but its also the farthest from the son

____

X. Use the dictionary entry to answer the questions.

rotunda (rō ten′ de) *n.* **1.** a round building, especially one covered by a dome. **2.** a large round room. [Latin *rotunda*]

at; **ā**pe; f**ä**r; c**â**re; **e**nd; m**ē**; **i**t; **ī**ce; p**î**erce; h**o**t; **ō**ld, s**ô**ng; f**ô**rk; **oi**l; **ou**t; **u**p; **ū**se; r**ü**le; p**u̇**ll; t**û**rn; **ch**in; si**ng**; **sh**op; **th**in; **th**is; **hw** in **wh**ite; **zh** in trea**s**ure. The symbol **ə** stands for the unstressed vowel sound in **a**bout, tak**e**n, penc**i**l, lem**o**n, and circ**u**s.

1. What part of speech is the word rotunda? ____________
2. Would rotunda come before or after rough in the dictionary? ____________
3. Which language is in the history of the word rotunda? ____________
4. Write the word for this respelling: (thot′ fu̇l)? ____________
5. Write rotunda separated into syllables. ____________

Y. Write the source from the box that you would use to find the information listed.

dictionary	card catalog	encyclopedia	atlas	*Readers' Guide*

____________ **1.** the pronunciation of a word

____________ **2.** the call numbers of a book

____________ **3.** an article on icebergs

____________ **4.** when an article was published in *Newsweek*

____________ **5.** a map of Australia

Below is a list of the sections on *Check What You've Learned* and the pages on which the skills in each section are taught. If you missed any questions, turn to the pages listed, and practice the skills. Then correct the problems you missed on *Check What You've Learned.*

Section	Practice Page
Unit 1	
A	5, 6
B	7
C	8, 9, 11
D	10
E	12
F	13
Unit 2	
G	18–20, 23
H	25, 26
I	24, 33, 35

Section	Practice Page
J	28, 30, 34
Unit 3	
K	41–45
L	48
M	49–53
N	55–61
O	65
P	66, 67
Q	68
R	69–73
S	74, 75, 77

Section	Practice Page
Unit 4	
T	82–90
Unit 5	
U	96–98
V	102, 103
W	104–105
Unit 6	
X	110–114
Y	116–127

Answer Key

Check What You Know (P. 1)

A. **1.** H **2.** A **3.** S **4.** S

B. lock

C. **1.** C **2.** P **3.** S **4.** P

D. **1.** they will **2.** we have

E. unhappy

F. 2

G. The words in bold should be circled.

1. IM; (You), **wait**
2. IN; you, **do believe**
3. E; I, **burned**
4. D; article, **made**

H. **1.** CP **2.** CS

I. **1.** I **2.** RO **3.** CS

J. [After I moved into town], I rented a beautiful new DO apartment.

Check What You Know (P. 2)

K. The words in bold should be circled.

Mayor Dumonte showed the citizens of our city that he was honest by appointing **Ms. Lopez** to the position.

L. The word in bold should be circled.

His favorite nurse, **Ms. Abram**, made his stay in the hospital more pleasant.

M. **1.** future **2.** present **3.** past

N. **1.** are, were **2.** saw, knew **3.** begun, went **4.** threw, broke

O. 2

P. The words in bold should be circled.

1. IP, **Somebody**
2. OP, **her**
3. PP, **their**
4. SP, **We**

Q. The word in bold should be circled.

The **jets** flew in their assigned formation.

R. **1.** adjective **2.** adverb **3.** adverb **4.** adjective

S. The words in bold should be circled.

The girl **on** the bus waved **at** me while it passed by.

Check What You Know (P. 3)

T.

956 E. Garden Circle
Bowman, TX 78787
April 13, 2006

Dear Steve,

We're so excited you're coming to visit! Even little Scott managed to say, "Uncle Steve visit," which was pretty good for a child of only twenty-two months, wouldn't you agree? Oh, I want to be sure I have the information correct. Please let me know as soon as possible if any of this is wrong: flight 561, arrive at 3:30 P.M., May 22, 2006. See you then.

Your sister,
Amanda

U. **1.** 3 **2.** 1 **3.** 4 **4.** 2

V. 2

Check What You Know (P. 4)

W. Although the decision to close Mayfield Park was unpopular, it proved to be the correct choice.

X. **1.** adjective **2.** before **3.** Middle English **4.** gaiety **5.** jol-ly

Y. **1.** *Readers' Guide* **2.** card catalog **3.** atlas **4.** dictionary **5.** encyclopedia

Vocabulary

Lesson 1, Synonyms and Antonyms (P. 5)

A. Discuss your answers with your instructor.

B. Discuss your answers with your instructor.

C. Discuss your answers with your instructor.

D. Discuss your answers with your instructor.

Lesson 2, Homonyms (P. 6)

A. **1.** two, past
2. too, to
3. hear
4. heard
5. not, know, not
6. seem, our
7. won, medal
8. weigh
9. air, so, need
10. rows
11. knew, new, feet
12. beet
13. not, scene
14. waist

B.
1. piece
2. alter
3. too or two
4. weigh or whey
5. beach
6. plane
7. course
8. seam
9. new
10. sail
11. so
12. brake
13. weak
14. rain or reign
15. bear
16. seen
17. might
18. hole
19. horse
20. forth
21. night
22. him
23. threw
24. groan
25. rap
26. pray
27. straight
28. soul
29. here
30. where, wear

Lesson 3, Homographs (P. 7)

A. **1.** b **2.** b **3.** a **4.** b

B.
1. checkers
2. duck
3. can
4. alight

C.
1. stall
2. snap
3. squash
4. quack
5. punch

Lesson 4, Prefixes (P. 8)

Discuss your answers with your instructor.

Lesson 5, Suffixes (P. 9)

Discuss your answers with your instructor.

Lesson 6, Contractions (P. 10)

A.
1. didn't
2. wasn't
3. we're
4. isn't
5. who's
6. hadn't
7. I'll
8. I'm
9. it's
10. don't
11. they've
12. wouldn't
13. won't
14. doesn't
15. weren't
16. there's
17. couldn't
18. I've
19. she'll
20. they're

B.
1. They're; They are
2. They'll; They will
3. it's; it is
4. Mary's; Mary is
5. she'll; she will
6. doesn't; does not; he's; he is
7. He'd; He would
8. would've; would have
9. aren't; are not; Tom's; Tom is
10. they've; they have

Lesson 7, Compound Words (P. 11)

A. Any twelve of the following words should be listed:

airline	underline	undersea
airport	doorway	blackbird
air-condition	understand	blackberry
sandpaper	seaport	seabird
doorknob	underground	

B. Discuss your answers with your instructor.

Lesson 8, Connotation/Denotation (P. 12)

A. **1.** N **2.** + **3.** N **4.** – **5.** N **6.** – **7.** N **8.** + **9.** – **10.** N

B.
1. horrible
2. exciting
3. unpleasant
4. old
5. mature
6. over-the-hill

Lesson 9, Idioms (P. 13)

A. Discuss your answers with your instructor.

1. in hot water
2. was beside herself
3. put their heads together
4. was all ears
5. throw in the towel

B. Discuss your answers with your instructor.

1. hit the road
2. eat crow
3. burn the midnight oil
4. cut me down to size

Review (P. 14)

A. **1.** A **2.** S **3.** S **4.** A **5.** A **6.** S **7.** A **8.** A **9.** S **10.** S **11.** A **12.** A

B.
1. weak, week
2. write, right
3. blew, blue
4. read, red
5. pain, pane

C. **1.** b **2.** b **3.** a **4.** b

D.
1. thankful
2. repay
3. disagree
4. foolish
5. blacken
6. thankless
7. unhappy
8. mistake

Review (P. 15)

E.
1. does not; doesn't
2. she would; she'd
3. It is; It's
4. does not; doesn't
5. must not; mustn't
6. Who is; Who's
7. did not; didn't

F.
1. doorknob
2. footstool
3. roadblock
4. sidewalk
5. greenhouse

G. **1.** – **2.** + **3.** – **4.** – **5.** + **6.** – **7.** – **8.** – **9.** + **10.** –

H. Discuss your answers with your instructor.

1. hit the high spots
2. cut corners
3. pull some strings

Using What You've Learned (P. 16)

A. **1.** S **2.** HM **3.** HG **4.** HM **5.** S **6.** A **7.** A

B. **1.** thankful; full of thanks
2. unhappy; not happy
3. displeased; not pleased
4. thankless; without thanks
5. repainted; painted again
6. transplant; Discuss your answers with your instructor.
7. unsure; not sure

C. **1.** will not **2.** I am **3.** it is **4.** were not **5.** she will **6.** we are

Using What You've Learned (P. 17)

D. **1.** N; – **2.** –; N **3.** N; – **4.** –; N **5.** N; – **6.** N; – **7.** N; – **8.** –; N

E. Discuss your answers with your instructor.

Unit 2 Sentences

Lesson 10, Recognizing Sentences (P. 18)

S should precede the following sentences, and each should end with a period: 1, 3, 5, 7, 10, 13, 14, 16, 17, 22, 23, 25, 28, 29, 30.

Lesson 11, Types of Sentences (P. 19)

A. **1.** D **2.** IM **3.** IN **4.** IM **5.** IN **6.** IN **7.** D **8.** IN **9.** IM **10.** E **11.** IM **12.** IN **13.** IN **14.** D **15.** IN **16.** IM **17.** IN **18.** IM **19.** IN **20.** IM or E **21.** D **22.** IN **23.** IM

Lesson 11, Types of Sentences (P. 20)

24. E **25.** IN **26.** IM or E **27.** IM **28.** D **29.** IM **30.** E **31.** IM **32.** D **33.** IN **34.** IM **35.** IM **36.** D **37.** D **38.** IN **39.** E **40.** IN **41.** D **42.** D **43.** E

B. The following sentences should be circled:

1. When will the train arrive? IN
2. It is delayed by bad weather. D
3. Juan and Shelly are on it. D
4. I haven't seen them in two years! E
5. They will stay with us for two weeks. D
6. We have many things planned for them. D
7. Sleep in the guest room. IM
8. Juan used to work at a zoo. D
9. Go in the reptile house. IM
10. Each elephant had a name. D
11. The elephants liked to train with Juan. D
12. Sandra, the elephant, had a baby. D
13. What did the zoo officials name the baby? IN
14. They surprised Juan! E
15. He never had an elephant named for him before! E

Lesson 12, Complete Subjects and Predicates (P. 21)

A.
1. Amy/built...
2. This cleaner/will...
3. Many beautiful waltzes/were...
4. Queen Victoria/ruled...
5. Eighty people/are...
6. Mario's last visit/was...
7. The rocket/was...
8. Our last meeting/was...
9. The farmers/are...
10. Our new house/has...
11. The heart/pumps...
12. This computer/will...
13. My friend/has...
14. A deep silence/fell...
15. The police officers/were...
16. The French chef/prepared...
17. My father/is...
18. José Salazar/is...
19. Lightning/struck...
20. Magazines about bicycling/are...
21. They/answered...
22. The gray twilight/came...
23. Steve/has...
24. That section of the country/has...
25. We/will...
26. Butterflies/flew...
27. The heavy bus/was...

Lesson 12, Complete Subjects and Predicates (P. 22)

B. Discuss your answers with your instructor.

C. Discuss your answers with your instructor.

Lesson 13, Simple Subjects and Predicates (P. 23)

A.
1. The plants/sprouted...
2. The television program/was...
3. I/used...

4. My friend's truck/is...
5. The beavers/created...
6. The books/lined...
7. Hail/pounded...
8. I/bought...
9. My favorite subject/is...
10. The colorful bird/sang...
11. The tree trunk/was...
12. The sidewalk/had...

B. 1. A rare Chinese vase/was on display.
2. Many of the children/had played.
3. All of the group/went on a hike.
4. He/drove the bus slowly over the slippery pavement.
5. A large number of water-skiers/were on the lake last Saturday.
6. Birds/have good eyesight.
7. Who/discovered the Pacific Ocean?
8. I/am reading the assignment now.
9. The glare of the headlights/blinded us.
10. The problem on the next page/is harder.

Lesson 14, Position of Subjects (P. 24)

1. The sunken treasure ship was where?
2. Several sailboats were beyond the bridge.
3. No one is in that room.
4. The shouts of the victorious team came from the gymnasium.
5. Beautiful flowers grew beside the walk.
6. The surprise party is when?
7. (You) Bring your sales report to the meeting.
8. Only three floats were in the parade.
9. The bark of the dog came from the yard.
10. (You) Place the forks to the left of the plate.

Lesson 15, Compound Subjects (P. 25)

A. Sentences 1, 3, 4, 6, 7, 8, 9, 10, 11, 13, 14, 15, 16, 18, 20, 21, and 22 have compound subjects. Sentences 2, 5, 12, 17, 19, 23, 24, and 25 have simple subjects.

1. Arturo and I/often...
2. Sandy/left...
3. She and I/will...
4. Shanghai and New Delhi/are...
5. The fire/spread...
6. Luis and Lenora/helped...
7. Swimming, jogging, and hiking/were...
8. Melbourne and Sydney/are...
9. Eric and I/had...
10. The Red Sea and the Mediterranean Sea/are...
11. The Republicans and the Democrats/made...
12. The people/waved...
13. Liz and Jim/crated...
14. Clean clothes and a neat appearance/are...
15. The kitten and the old dog/are...
16. David and Paul/are...
17. Tom/combed...
18. Redbud and dogwood trees/bloom...
19. I/hummed...
20. Buffalo, deer, and antelope/once...
21. Gina and Hiroshi/raked...
22. Brasília and São Paulo/are...
23. Hang gliding/is...
24. Our class/went...
25. The doctor/asked...

B. Discuss your answers with your instructor.

Lesson 16, Compound Predicates (P. 26)

A. Sentences 1, 4, 6, 9, 10, 12, 13, 18, 19, 20, 22, and 23 have compound predicates. Sentences 2, 3, 5, 7, 8, 11, 14, 15, 16, 17, 21, 24, and 25 have simple predicates.

1. Edward/grinned and nodded.
2. Plants/need air to live.
3. Old silver tea kettles/were among their possessions.
4. My sister/buys and sells real estate.
5. Snow/covered every highway in the area.
6. Mr. Sanders/designs and makes odd pieces of furniture.
7. Popcorn/is one of my favorite snack foods.
8. Soccer/is one of my favorite sports.
9. The ducks/quickly crossed the road and found the ducklings.
10. They/came early and stayed late.
11. Crystal/participated in the Special Olympics this year.
12. José/raked and sacked the leaves.
13. Perry/built the fire and cooked supper.
14. We/collected old newspapers for the recycling center.
15. Doug/arrived in Toronto, Ontario, during the afternoon.
16. Tony's parents/are visiting in Oregon and Washington.
17. The Garzas/live in that apartment building on Oak Street.
18. The shingles/were picked up and delivered today.
19. The audience/talked and laughed before the performance.
20. Automobiles/crowd and jam that highway early in the morning.

21. The apples/are rotting in the boxes.
22. The leader of the group/grumbled and scolded.
23. She/worked hard and waited patiently.
24. Nelson Mandela/is a great civil rights activist.
25. The supervisor/has completed the work for the week.

B. Sentences will vary.

Lesson 17, Combining Sentences (P. 27)

1. Lightning and thunder are part of a thunderstorm.
2. Thunderstorms usually happen in the spring and bring heavy rains.
3. Depending on how close or far away it is, thunder sounds like a sharp crack or rumbles.
4. Lightning is very exciting to watch and can be very dangerous.
5. Lightning causes many fires and harms many people.
6. An open field or a golf course is an unsafe place to be during a thunderstorm.
7. Benjamin Franklin wanted to protect people from lightning and invented the lightning rod.
8. A lightning rod is a metal rod placed on the top of a building and connected to the ground by a cable.

Lesson 18, Direct Objects (P. 28)

1. Elephants can carry logs (DO) with their trunks.
2. Who made this magazine rack (DO)?
3. Do you always plan a daily schedule (DO)?
4. They easily won the game (DO).
5. Martin baked an apple pie (DO) for dinner.
6. Who tuned your piano (DO)?
7. I take guitar lessons (DO) once a week.
8. Who composed this melody (DO)?
9. I especially enjoy mystery stories (DO).
10. The astronauts orbited the earth (DO) many times.
11. I bought this coat (DO) in New York.
12. Did he find his glasses (DO)?
13. Anne drove the truck (DO) to the hardware store.
14. The boy shrugged his shoulders (DO).
15. We have finished our work (DO) today.
16. We drink milk (DO) with breakfast.
17. She can solve any problem (DO) quickly.
18. Who made our first flag (DO)?
19. You will learn something (DO) from this lesson.
20. Every person needs friends (DO).
21. I have found a dime (DO).
22. Yuko ate an apple (DO) for a snack.

Lesson 19, Indirect Objects (P. 29)

1. Certain marine plants give the Red Sea (IO) its color (DO).
2. I gave the cashier (IO) a check (DO) for twenty dollars.
3. The magician showed the audience (IO) a few of her tricks (DO).
4. The coach taught them (IO) the rules (DO) of the game.
5. Roberto brought us (IO) some foreign coins (DO).
6. This interesting book will give every reader (IO) pleasure (DO).
7. Have you written your brother (IO) a letter (DO)?
8. They made us (IO) some sandwiches (DO) to take on our hike.
9. The astronaut gave Mission Control (IO) the data (DO).
10. I bought my friend (IO) an etching (DO) at the art exhibit.
11. James, did you sell Mike (IO) your car (DO)?
12. We have given the dog (IO) a thorough scrubbing (DO).
13. Give the usher (IO) your ticket (DO).
14. Carl brought my brother (IO) a gold ring (DO) from Mexico.
15. Hand me (IO) a pencil (DO), please.
16. The conductor gave the orchestra (IO) a short break (DO).
17. Show me (IO) the picture (DO) of your boat.
18. I have given you (IO) my money (DO).
19. Give Lee (IO) this message (DO).
20. The club gave the town (IO) a new statue (DO).

Lesson 20, Independent and Subordinate Clauses (P. 30)

A. 1. Frank will be busy because he is studying.
2. I have only one hour that I can spare.

3. The project must be finished when I get back.
4. Gloria volunteered to do the typing that needs to be done.
5. The work is going too slowly for us to finish on time.
6. Before Nathan started to help, I didn't think we could finish.
7. What else should we do before we relax?
8. Since you forgot to give this page to Gloria, you can type it.
9. After she had finished typing, we completed the project.
10. We actually got it finished before the deadline.

B.
1. The people who went shopping found a great sale.
2. Tony's bike, which is a mountain bike, came from that store.
3. Juana was sad when the sale was over.
4. Marianne was excited because she wanted some new things.
5. Thomas didn't find anything since he went late.
6. The mall where we went shopping was new.
7. The people who own the stores are proud of the beautiful setting.
8. The mall, which is miles away, is serviced by the city bus.
9. We ran as fast as we could because the bus was coming.
10. We were panting because we had run fast.

Lesson 21, Adjective Clauses (P. 31)

A.
1. A compass has a needle that always points northward.
2. A seismograph is an instrument that measures earthquake tremors.
3. People who work in science laboratories today have a broad field of study.
4. This will be the first time that she has played in that position.
5. Jay is the person whose wrist was broken.
6. The fish that I caught was large.
7. A sentence that contains a subordinate clause is a complex sentence.
8. Here is the photograph that I promised to show you.
9. The book that I read was very humorous.

B. Discuss your answers with your instructor.

Lesson 22, Adverb Clauses (P. 32)

A.
1. We had agreed to go hiking when the cloudy skies cleared.
2. Although the weather was mild and sunny, we took along our jackets.
3. Clouds began to move in once again after we arrived at the park.
4. We felt comfortable about the weather because we were prepared.
5. Since we had our jackets, we didn't get too cold.
6. Although the clouds remained, it never rained.
7. It was exhilarating to see the view when we got to the top of the hill.
8. After enjoying the beauty and the quiet for a while, we hiked back down.
9. We decided to drive home the long way since it was still early.
10. We had a wonderful day because we were so relaxed and happy.

B. Discuss your answers with your instructor.

Lesson 23, Simple and Compound Sentences (P. 33)

A. Sentences 2, 3, 5, and 8 are simple sentences.

Sentences 1, 4, 6, and 7 are compound sentences.

B.
1. [You must observe all the rules,] or [you must withdraw from the race.]
2. [I did well on the test,] and [Maria did well, too.]
3. [Shall I carry this box,] or [do you want to leave it here?]
4. [We must closely guard our freedom,] or [an enemy will take it from us.]
5. [He threw a beautiful pass,] but [no one caught it.]
6. [The doctor treated the cut,] but [he did not have to make any stitches.]
7. [I like to spend weekends at home,] but [the others prefer to travel.]
8. [The year is almost over,] and [everyone is thinking of the new year.]
9. [The family faced every hardship,] yet [they were thankful for what they had.]
10. [Move the box over here]; [I'll unpack it.]
11. [Connie likes football]; [James prefers hockey.]
12. [I drive safely,] but [I always make everyone fasten seat belts.]
13. [Please get the telephone number,] and [I'll call after work.]

Lesson 24, Complex Sentences (P. 34)

A.
1. The shadows [that had fallen between the trees] were a deep purple.
2. The soldiers waded across the stream [where the water was shallow.]
3. They waited for me [until the last bus came.]
4. The fans of that team were sad [when the team lost the game.]
5. [When George was here,] he was charmed by the beauty of the hills.

6. Sophia will call for you [when she is ready.]
7. Some spiders [that are found in Sumatra] have legs seventeen inches long.
8. Those [who are going] will arrive on time.
9. Do not throw the bat [after you've hit the ball.]
10. Tell us about the trip [that you made a year ago.]

B. Discuss your answers with your instructor.

Lesson 25, Correcting Run-on Sentences (P. 35)

Sentences will vary. Suggested:

1. The city council held a meeting. A meeting is held every month.
2. The council members are elected by the voters; there are two thousand voters in the city.
3. There is one council member from each suburb, and the president is elected by the council members.
4. Those who run for office must give speeches. The speeches should be short.
5. The council decides on many activities, and every activity is voted on.
6. Money is needed for many of the special activities, so the council plans fund-raisers in the city.
7. The annual city picnic is sponsored by the city council. The picnic is in May.

Lesson 26, Expanding Sentences (P. 36)

A. Discuss your answers with your instructor.

B. Discuss your answers with your instructor.

Review (P. 37)

A.
1. IN; ?
2. E; ! or IM; .
3. X
4. D; .
5. E; !
6. IN; ?
7. E; !
8. X
9. D; .
10. IM; .

B.
1. The lights around the public square went out.
2. Stations are in all parts of our country.
3. Carmen collects fans for a hobby.
4. We drove slowly across the bridge.
5. We saw an unusual flower.
6. Taro swims and dives quite well.
7. The cake and bread are kept in the box.
8. The referee gave our team a fifteen-yard penalty.
9. A good citizen obeys the laws, but a bad citizen doesn't.
10. Please lend me your raincoat, so I can stay dry.

C.
1. CX
2. CP
3. CX
4. CP
5. CX
6. CX
7. CX
8. CP
9. CX
10. CP

Review (P. 38)

D.
1. The director gave the actors (IO) a new script (DO).
2. Jenny showed her friends (IO) her vacation slides (DO).
3. Ms. Lopez took her sick neighbor (IO) some chicken soup (DO).
4. We handed the cashier (IO) our money (DO).
5. Enrique, please give your brother (IO) his jacket (DO).

E. The words in bold should be circled.
1. The campers got wet **when it started raining**.
2. The candidates **that I voted for in the election** won easily.
3. **Before the board voted on the issue**, it held public hearings.
4. The freeway through town is a road **where vehicles often speed**.
5. **While we waited**, the children kept us entertained.

F.
1. who are trained in weather forecasting; adjective clause
2. Before I decided on a college; adverb clause
3. that I designed; adjective clause
4. Although the furniture was old; adverb clause
5. because they want to stay healthy; adverb clause
6. before I left; adverb clause

G.
1. A large goldfish lay just below the surface.
2. The baseball flew over the roof.

H.
1. Dogs are Erica's favorite animal, and cats are John's favorite animal.
2. The water reflected the sun, so we put on our sunglasses.

Using What You've Learned (P. 39)

A.
1. D
2. E
3. A
4. A
5. A
6. D, E
7. B
8. C
9. We
10. We
11. Be at my house by seven o'clock .

B. The words in bold should be circled.
1. The streamers sagged **after we hung them**.
2. Mark knows party planning **because he has many parties**.
3. Everyone **who wants to go to the party** must bring something.

4. **If everyone brings something,** the party will be great.
5. **Unless I am wrong,** the party is tomorrow.
6. **As if everything had been done,** Jake ran out of the room.
7. The girls **who planned the party** received roses.
8. I will never forget the day **that I fell on my face at a party**.

C. Sentences may vary. Suggested:

1. The team sat in the dugout, and the fans sat in the stands.
2. The rain finally stopped, so the game continued.
3. It was the bottom of the ninth inning; there were two outs.
4. The batter swung at the pitch, and the umpire called, "Strike three!"

Using What You've Learned (P. 40)

D. 1. Two seagulls perched on the rocks.
2. The supplies for the office are here.

E. Discuss your answers with your instructor.

F. Patricia didn't know what to do. She had a terrible problem, and she was trying to solve it. No matter how hard she thought about it, no answers seemed to come. She decided to take a break and not think about it for a while. She went to the mall, where she always enjoyed browsing in the bookstore. She wasn't even thinking about the problem; the answer just popped into her head. She was so excited about solving her problem that she completely forgot about the bookstore.

G. Discuss your answers with your instructor.

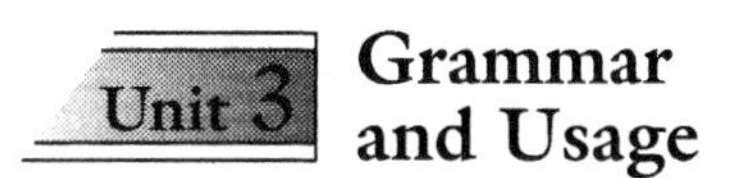

Grammar and Usage

Lesson 27, Nouns (P. 41)

1. Lupe Garcia; years; supervisor
2. piece; land; mouth; river, delta
3. Gilbert Stuart; artist; portraits; presidents
4. Albert Einstein; scientist; century; Germany
5. library, world; Alexandria, Egypt
6. Jim Thorpe; Oklahoma; athletes; world
7. Mahalia Jackson; singer; spirituals
8. Marconi; telegraph
9. parades; games; television; New Year's Day
10. Terry Fox; runner; leg; cancer; miles; Canada
11. *Boston News-Letter*; newspaper; United States
12. message; English Channel; century
13. Chicago; city; Lake Michigan
14. seat; window
15. Kuang; house
16. children; trip; Carlsbad Caverns
17. Washington, D.C.; capital; United States
18. France; food; country; Europe
19. Maria; car
20. Hailstones; raindrops; snowflakes
21. days; summer
22. rivers, explorers
23. Jeff; carport; boat
24. California; home; stars
25. William Caxton; book; England
26. Chris; tomatoes; lettuce; cherries; market
27. building, offices; stores; apartments
28. Leticia; Peoria; Illinois; friend
29. airport; hours; snowstorm
30. pen; ink

Lesson 28, Common and Proper Nouns (P. 42)

A. The words in bold should be circled.

1. story; prince; pauper; clothing
2. **New York**; **Los Angeles**; cities; **United States**
3. story; **Scrooge**; **Tiny Tim**
4. **Sumatra**; island; **Indian Ocean**
5. **United States**; hail; damage; tornadoes
6. paper; **Chinese**
7. **Rikki-tikki-tavi**; **Rudyard Kipling**; story; mongoose
8. ***Shamrock***; name; emblem; **Ireland**
9. shilling; coin; **England**
10. lights; car; pavement
11. **Nathan**; **Sam**; **Tuesday**
12. **Great Sphinx**, monument; **Egypt**
13. family; **Mexico**; **Canada**; year

B. Answers will vary. Suggested:

1. country	8. planet	15. college
2. book	9. person	16. mountains
3. person	10. continent	17. person
4. state	11. inventor	18. lake
5. composer	12. continent	19. day
6. ocean	13. month	20. holiday
7. country	14. city	

Lesson 28, Common and Proper Nouns (P. 43)

C. Discuss your answers with your instructor.

D. Discuss your answers with your instructor.

Lesson 29, Singular and Plural Nouns (P. 44)

A. 1. brushes 3. countries 5. earrings
2. lunches 4. benches 6. calves

7. pianos
8. foxes
9. daisies
10. potatoes
11. dishes
12. stores

Lesson 29, Singular and Plural Nouns (P. 45)

B.
1. booklets
2. tomatoes
3. trucks
4. chefs
5. branches
6. toddlers
7. pennies
8. potatoes
9. pieces
10. doors
11. islands
12. countries
13. houses
14. garages
15. fish
16. watches
17. elves
18. desks
19. pans
20. sheep
21. gardens
22. ponies
23. solos
24. trees
25. lights
26. churches
27. cities
28. spoonfuls
29. vacations
30. homes

C.
1. Put the apples and oranges in the boxes.
2. Jan wrote five letters to her friends.
3. Those buildings each have four elevators.
4. Our families drove many miles to get to the lakes.
5. The tops of those cars were damaged in the storms.
6. My aunts and uncles attended the family reunion.

Lesson 30, Possessive Nouns (P. 46)

A.
1. brother's
2. boy's
3. Carol's
4. children's
5. grandmother's
6. men's
7. heroes'
8. women's
9. ox's
10. man's
11. Dr. Kahn's
12. soldier's
13. pony's
14. friend's
15. child's
16. engineers'
17. birds'
18. Jon's

B. Discuss your answers with your instructor.

Lesson 30, Possessive Nouns (P. 47)

C.
1. doctor's
2. senator's
3. sheep's
4. baby's
5. instructor's
6. collectors'
7. spider's
8. Mr. Takata's
9. Tim's
10. Beth's
11. Carl Sandburg's
12. child's
13. women's
14. elephants'
15. sister's
16. Brazil's
17. friends'
18. bird's
19. children's
20. owl's
21. brothers'
22. student's
23. country's
24. owner's
25. uncle's
26. Joan's
27. men's

Lesson 31, Appositives (P. 48)

A. The words in bold should be circled.

1. **Banff**, the large Canadian national park
2. **painter**, Vincent Van Gogh
3. **White House**, home of the President of the United States
4. **Uncle Marco**, my mother's brother
5. **Earth**, the only inhabited planet in our solar system
6. **scorpion**, a native of the southwestern part of North America
7. **cat**, Amelia
8. **Judge Andropov**, the presiding judge
9. **friend**, Luisa

B. Discuss your answers with your instructor.

Lesson 32, Action Verbs (P. 49)

1. Watch
2. dusted
3. copy
4. burned
5. fell
6. play
7. practiced
8. dashed
9. expresses
10. enjoys
11. leads
12. snowed
13. hiked
14. made
15. hand
16. Draw
17. skated
18. answered
19. repaired
20. suffered
21. Write
22. moved
23. worked
24. directs
25. played
26. walked
27. helped
28. collapsed
29. ticked

Lesson 33, Linking Verbs (P. 50)

A.
1. appears
2. is
3. was
4. is
5. looks
6. are
7. smell
8. feels
9. sounds
10. seems

B. Discuss your answers with your instructor.

Lesson 34, Principal Parts of Verbs (P. 51)

1. is stopping; stopped; (have, has, had) stopped
2. is listening; listened; (have, has, had) listened
3. is carrying; carried; (have, has, had) carried
4. is helping; helped; (have, has, had) helped
5. is starting; started; (have, has, had) started
6. is borrowing; borrowed; (have, has, had) borrowed
7. is calling; called; (have, has, had) called
8. is receiving; received; (have, has, had) received
9. is hoping; hoped; (have, has, had) hoped
10. is illustrating; illustrated; (have, has, had) illustrated
11. is dividing; divided; (have, has, had) divided
12. is changing; changed; (have, has, had) changed
13. is scoring; scored; (have, has, had) scored
14. is ironing; ironed; (have, has, had) ironed
15. is studying; studied; (have, has, had) studied
16. is collecting; collected; (have, has, had) collected
17. is laughing; laughed; (have, has, had) laughed

Lesson 35, Verb Phrases (P. 52)

A. Discuss your answers with your instructor.

B.
1. has returned
2. has planned
3. would have answered
4. have been looking
5. have asked
6. have organized
7. has been planned
8. must speak
9. were dimmed
10. had been seen
11. were threatened
12. are planning

Lesson 36, Verb Tenses (P. 53)

A. Discuss your answers with your instructor.

B.
1. future
2. past
3. future
4. present
5. past
6. past
7. present
8. future
9. past
10. past

Lesson 37, Present Perfect and Past Perfect Tenses (P. 54)

A.
1. past perfect
2. past perfect
3. present perfect
4. past perfect
5. present perfect
6. present perfect
7. present perfect
8. past perfect
9. present perfect
10. present perfect

B.
1. has
2. have
3. had
4. has
5. had
6. has
7. had

Lesson 38, Using *Is/Are* and *Was/Were* (P. 55)

1. is
2. are
3. is
4. is
5. are
6. is
7. are
8. Are
9. is
10. are
11. were; was
12. were
13. was
14. were
15. were
16. weren't
17. weren't
18. were
19. weren't
20. were
21. was
22. was
23. was
24. Were
25. were
26. Weren't
27. were
28. Were
29. were

Lesson 39, Past Tenses of *Give, Take,* and *Write* (P. 56)

A.
1. took
2. taken
3. wrote
4. written
5. gave
6. given
7. written
8. written
9. given
10. wrote
11. taken
12. taken
13. gave
14. took
15. given
16. written
17. took
18. gave
19. written

B.
1. took
2. written
3. gave
4. given
5. taken
6. took
7. gave
8. taken

Lesson 40, Past Tenses of *See, Go,* and *Begin* (P. 57)

A.
1. saw
2. gone
3. began
4. went
5. begun
6. seen
7. gone
8. saw
9. seen
10. went
11. begun
12. began
13. gone
14. began
15. begun
16. saw
17. went
18. seen
19. went
20. began
21. began

B. Discuss your answers with your instructor.

Lesson 41, *Wear, Rise, Steal, Choose,* and *Break* (P. 58)

A.
1. worn
2. chosen
3. broke
4. rose
5. stolen
6. chosen
7. worn
8. rose
9. stolen
10. rose
11. worn
12. chose
13. broken
14. stolen
15. risen
16. broken
17. wore
18. risen
19. stole

B. The following verbs should be circled:
had rose
had stole
worn
chosen
had broke

Lesson 42, *Come, Ring, Drink, Know,* and *Throw* (P. 59)

A.
1. drank
2. rung
3. drunk
4. knew
5. thrown
6. come
7. rang
8. known
9. threw
10. came
11. drunk
12. come
13. knew
14. thrown
15. come
16. rang
17. drank

B. Discuss your answers with your instructor.

Lesson 43, *Eat, Fall, Draw, Drive,* and *Run* (P. 60)

A.
1. drawn
2. driven; began
3. fallen
4. eaten; ran
5. drew
6. run
7. fallen; ran
8. fallen
9. drove
10. eaten
11. ate
12. fallen
13. ran

B.
1. drove
2. drew
3. fallen
4. fell
5. driven
6. ran
7. ate
8. eaten
9. drawn
10. run

Lesson 44, Forms of *Do* (P. 61)

A.
1. doesn't
2. did
3. done
4. doesn't
5. did
6. Don't
7. done
8. Don't
9. doesn't
10. don't
11. done
12. did
13. Doesn't
14. Doesn't
15. done
16. doesn't

B. Discuss your answers with your instructor.

C. Discuss your answers with your instructor.

Lesson 45, Transitive and Intransitive Verbs (P. 62)

A.
1. joined; T
2. wanted; T
3. exercised; I
4. became; I
5. worked; I
6. preferred; T
7. liked; T
8. switched; I
9. took; T
10. used; T
11. swam; I
12. was; T
13. had; T
14. splashed; I

B. The words in bold should be circled.
1. walked; **Tiny**
2. pulled; **Carlos**
3. washed; **Tiny**
4. loved; **water**
5. splashed; **Carlos**
6. loved; **bones**
7. chewed; **bones**
8. found; **Tiny**

Lesson 46, Verbals (P. 63)

A.
1. to quit
2. to finish
3. to run
4. to win
5. to finish
6. to accomplish
7. to see

B.
1. yelling
2. excited
3. running
4. marching
5. Chosen
6. flashing
7. interested

C.
1. Studying
2. reading
3. Learning
4. Memorizing
5. Remembering
6. studying
7. Dancing

Lesson 46, Verbals (P. 64)

D.
1. infinitive; To act
2. gerund; Acting
3. infinitive; To write
4. gerund; Working
5. infinitive; to participate
6. participle; hurried
7. participle; moving
8. infinitive; to read
9. gerund; Auditioning
10. participle; stirring
11. gerund; Rehearsing
12. infinitive; to memorize
13. participle; convincing
14. gerund; performing
15. participle; smiling
16. infinitive; To act
17. participle; budding
18. gerund; Performing
19. gerund; Bowing
20. gerund; playing
21. infinitive; To continue
22. gerund; Acting
23. participle; Interrupted
24. gerund; acting
25. infinitive; to excel
26. participle; Well-rehearsed

Lesson 47, Active and Passive Voice (P. 65)

A.
1. A
2. A
3. A
4. A
5. P
6. A
7. P
8. P
9. P
10. A

B. Discuss your answers with your instructor.

C. Discuss your answers with your instructor.

Lesson 48, Pronouns (P. 66)

A.
1. me
2. them
3. me
4. my
5. he
6. she
7. they
8. us
9. her
10. someone
11. I
12. your
13. He
14. me
15. Who
16. they
17. Everyone
18. their
19. Whom
20. she
21. hers
22. Who
23. ours
24. who

Lesson 48, Pronouns (P. 67)

B.
1. I; you; him; our
2. Who
3. They; us; we; their
4. you; me; I; them
5. He; us
6. My; our
7. Whom; you
8. you; me
9. They; us
10. his
11. Who; them
12. She; my; who
13. mine
14. Someone; them
15. Who; she
16. She; us
17. who
18. she; you
19. Who; me
20. we; them
21. Which; your
22. I; you; our
23. Which; mine
24. you; your
25. you; us
26. anybody
27. You; I
28. you; him

C. Discuss your answers with your instructor.

Lesson 49, Antecedents (P. 68)

A. The words in bold should be circled.

1. **Mike**; he
2. **Carmen**; her
3. **Carmen**; her
4. **Mike**; his
5. **Carmen**; her; **math**; it
6. **Mike and Carmen**; they
7. **test**; it
8. **class**; its
9. **palms**; they
10. **teacher**; he
11. **test**; it
12. **student**; his or her; **test**; it
13. **tests**; them
14. **Carmen**; her

B. 1. their 2. him 3. its 4. his 5. they 6. his 7. its 8. their 9. her 10. their

Lesson 50, Adjectives (P. 69)

A. Discuss your answers with your instructor.

B.
1. This; old; comfortable
2. a; funny
3. This; heavy; many; dangerous
4. The; eager; odd; every
5. The; tired; thirsty
6. This; favorite
7. The; solitary; the; lonely
8. the; sixth
9. These; damp
10. French
11. those
12. A; red; the; tall
13. The; heavy
14. A; tour; the
15. The; gorgeous; Italian
16. fresh
17. mashed; baked
18. Chinese

Lesson 51, Demonstrative Adjectives (P. 70)

1. those
2. That
3. those
4. those
5. That
6. Those
7. those
8. those
9. these
10. those
11. these
12. these
13. those
14. this
15. Those
16. these
17. those
18. That
19. These
20. those
21. these
22. these
23. These
24. those
25. Those

Lesson 52, Comparing with Adjectives (P. 71)

1. more changeable
2. most faithful
3. more agreeable
4. busiest
5. longer
6. loveliest
7. freshest
8. higher
9. more enjoyable
10. most reckless
11. youngest
12. tallest
13. more difficult
14. quietest

Lesson 53, Adverbs (P. 72)

A.
1. slowly; clearly; expressively
2. too; recklessly
3. slowly; quickly
4. too; harshly
5. here
6. everywhere
7. suddenly; quickly; around
8. too; rapidly
9. well
10. soundly
11. noisily
12. early
13. severely
14. quickly; steadily

B. Discuss your answers with your instructor.

Lesson 54, Comparing with Adverbs (P. 73)

A. 1. sooner 2. soonest 3. hard 4. more 5. faster 6. most

B.
1. fastest
2. faster
3. more seriously
4. most frequently
5. more quickly
6. most promptly
7. more promptly
8. most eagerly
9. more carefully
10. hardest

Lesson 55, Prepositions (P. 74)

1. of
2. of
3. in
4. For
5. At; to; about
6. of
7. beside
8. of
9. to; at; of
10. in; in
11. of; during; of
12. of; at
13. at; near
14. on; for
15. with
16. behind
17. in
18. of; on; behind
19. to; during
20. down
21. across; in
22. over; into
23. of; under
24. below; of
25. behind
26. of; by
27. between
28. for

Lesson 56, Prepositional Phrases (P. 75)

The words in bold should be circled.

1. The airplane was flying (above the **clouds**).
2. We are moving (to **North Carolina**).
3. Sandra lives (on the second **block**).
4. An old water tower once stood (on that **hill**).
5. The car slid (on the wet **pavement**).
6. Sealing wax was invented (in the seventeenth **century**).
7. Motto rings were first used (by the **Romans**).
8. Tungsten, a metal, was discovered (in **1781**).
9. Roses originally came (from **Asia**).
10. The ball rolled (into the **street**).
11. Do you always keep the puppies (in a **pen**)?
12. The children climbed (over the **fence**).
13. She lives (in **Denver, Colorado**).
14. Columbus made three trips (to **North America**).
15. They spread the lunch (under the **shade**) (of the giant elm **tree**).
16. The treasure was found (by a scuba **diver**).
17. A squad (of **soldiers**) marched (behind the **tank**).
18. Shall I row (across the **stream**)?
19. Large airplanes fly (across the **nation**).
20. Walter looked (into the **sack**).
21. The cat ran (up the **pole**).
22. We visited the Alexander Graham Bell Museum (in **Nova Scotia**).
23. Many tourists come (to our **region**).
24. We spent last summer (in the **Adirondack Mountains**).
25. Do not stand (behind a parked **car**).

Lesson 57, Prepositional Phrases as Adjectives and Adverbs (P. 76)

1. to the ranch; adverb
2. in French; adverb
3. in Tennessee; adjective
4. to the public library; adverb
5. in an old house; adverb
6. with red trim; adjective
7. in the zoo; adjective
8. in Myanmar; adverb
9. of my money; adjective
10. over the hat; adverb
11. of a Sequoia tree trunk; adjective
12. of New York; adjective
13. near the docks; adverb
14. to the movie; adverb
15. in 1911; adverb
16. in this room; adjective
17. across the yard; adverb
18. of petrified wood; adjective
19. across the lawn; adverb

Lesson 58, Conjunctions (P. 77)

1.	whether	**8.**	and
2.	and	**9.**	and
3.	when	**10.**	because
4.	or	**11.**	but
5.	and	**12.**	and
6.	unless	**13.**	because
7.	or	**14.**	since
15.	but	**21.**	for
16.	Although	**22.**	while
17.	than	**23.**	not only/but also
18.	neither/nor	**24.**	either/or
19.	either/or	**25.**	neither/nor
20.	but	**26.**	Neither/nor

Review (P. 78)

A. The underlined words should be labeled as follows:

1. A heavy (adj.) dust storm (n.) rolled (v.) across (prep.) the prairie (n.).
2. This is a (adj.) nice (adj.) surprise (n.)!
3. The dark (adj.) clouds (n.) slowly (adv.) gathered (v.) in the north.
4. Marlee (n.) and I (pron.) are showing slides of (prep.) the photographs that we (pron.) took on our trip (n.).
5. Is the capital (n.) of (prep.) your (pron.) state built on a river (n.)?
6. These (adj.) shrubs are (v.) beautiful (adj.).
7. Someone (pron.) opened the door very (adv.) cautiously (adv.) and (conj.) tiptoed inside.
8. Please handle (v.) this (adj.) extremely (adv.) fragile china very (adv.) carefully.
9. The (adj.) weary people (n.) waited for (prep.) the long (adj.) parade (n.) to start.
10. Large (adj.) herds of longhorn (adj.) cattle grazed on these (pron.) vast (adj.) plains.
11. We (pron.) are going to (prep.) the new (adj.) mall (n.) today (adv.), but (conj.) Sara can't go with us.
12. Floyd (n.), you (pron.) are eating that (adj.) food too (adv.) rapidly (adv.).

B.
1. bench's
2. flies
3. hero's
4. pony's
5. watch's

C. The words in bold should be circled.

1. **Ottawa**, the capital of Canada
2. **sister**, Kira
3. **breakfast**, pancakes and ham

Review (P. 79)

D.
1. gave
2. rang
3. come
4. known
5. drive
6. eaten
7. ran
8. went
9. doesn't
10. took
11. did
12. are
13. were
14. begun
15. fallen
16. wasn't

E.
1. to fish, infinitive
2. Skating, gerund
3. flashing, participle
4. to finish, infinitive
5. improved, participle

F. The words in bold should be circled.
1. he, **Mark**
2. their, **workers**
3. their, **Bob and Andre**
4. her, **sister**
5. them, **donations**

Using What You've Learned (P. 80)

B. she, her, it

C. Discuss your answers with your instructor.

D. Discuss your answers with your instructor.

E. Discuss your answers with your instructor.

F. Discuss your answers with your instructor.

G. Discuss your answers with your instructor.

Using What You've Learned (P. 81)

H. The first pilots of a motor-powered airplane were the Wright brothers, Orville and Wilbur. On December 17, 1903, the Wrights successfully flew their plane, Flyer 1, for the first time. The gasoline-powered plane was in the air for a total of 12 seconds. Another flight that day lasted 59 seconds and went 852 feet.

The Wright brothers spent many years perfecting their airplane designs. They were gifted engineers and already had built printing machinery, bicycles, and gliders. Their breakthrough came when they observed the way a buzzard controls its flight. They continued to improve on their airplane designs over the next few years. They eventually sold the first military airplane to the United States Army in 1909. Eventually, European mechanics produced more advanced airplanes than the Wrights' airplanes.

Capitalization and Punctuation

Lesson 59, Using Capital Letters (P. 82)

A. The first letter in each of the following should be circled and capitalized:
1. What
2. Francis; The; Star; Spangled; Banner
3. Edgar; The; Raven
4. Paul; When
5. Who; Snowbound; The; Barefoot; Boy
6. What; Give

B. The first letter in each of the following should be circled and capitalized:
1. Miami; Florida; Atlanta; Georgia
2. Potomac; River; Virginia; Maryland
3. *Pinta*; *Niña*; *Santa*; *María*; Columbus
4. Spanish; Mississippi; River; English; Jamestown
5. American; Red; Cross; Clara; Barton
6. Rocky; Mountains; Andes; Mountains; Alps

Lesson 59, Using Capital Letters (P. 83)

C. The first letter in each of the following should be circled and capitalized:
1. Dr.; Thompson
2. Mayor; Thomas
3. Dr.; Crawford; W.; Long
4. Mr.; Mrs.; Randall
5. Senator; Dixon
6. Gov.; Alden
7. Ms.; Howell

D. The first letter in each of the following should be circled and capitalized:
1. Niles School Art Fair
Sat., Feb. 8th, 9 A.M.
110 N. Elm Dr.
2. Shoreville Water Festival
June 23–24
Mirror Lake
Shoreville, MN 55108
3. October Fest
October 28 and 29
9 A.M.–5 P.M.
63 Maple St.
4. Barbara Dumont
150 Telson Rd.
Markham, Ontario L3R 1E5
5. Captain C. J. Neil
c/o Ocean Star
P. O. Box 4455
Portsmouth, NH 03801
6. Dr. Charles B. Stevens
Elmwood Memorial Hospital
1411 First Street
Tucson, AZ 85062

Lesson 59, Using Capital Letters (P. 84)

E. Discuss your answers with your instructor.

Lesson 60, Using End Punctuation (P. 85)

A.
1. ?
2. .
3. ?
4. ?
5. .
6. .
7. ?
8. ?
9. .
10. .
11. ?
12. .
13. ?
14. ?

B.
Line 1. ?
Line 2. .; .
Line 3. ?; .
Line 4. .; .
Line 5. .; ?
Line 6. .
Line 7. .; .
Line 9. .
Line 10. .; .
Line 11. .
Line 12. .; .; ?
Line 13. .

Lesson 60, Using End Punctuation (P. 86)

C.
1. .
2. .
3. !; . or !
4. !; .
5. .
6. .
7. . or !
8. !
9. !; !; !
10. .
11. .
12. !
13. ! or .
14. .
15. .
16. !
17. .
18. !; .

D.
Line 1. .
Line 2. !; ?
Line 3. .
Line 4. . or !
Line 5. .
Line 6. .
Line 7. !; .
Line 8. .
Line 9. .
Line 10. ?
Line 11. .; .

Lesson 61, Using Commas (P. 87)

A.
1. Frank, Mary, and Patricia are planning a surprise party for their parents.
2. It is their parents' fiftieth wedding anniversary, and the children want it to be special.
3. They have invited the people their father used to work with, their mother's garden club members, and long-time friends of the family.
4. Even though the children are grown and living in their own homes, it will be hard to make it a surprise.
5. Mr. and Mrs. Slaughter are active, friendly, and involved in many things.
6. For the surprise party to work, everyone will have to be sure not to say anything about their plans for that day.
7. This will be especially hard for the Knudsens, but they will do their best.
8. Since every Sunday the families have dinner together, the Knudsens will have to become very good actors the week of the party.

B.
1. "We're sorry that we have to cancel our plans," said Earl.
2. Carmen said, "But we've done this every week for ten years!"
3. Jeannette said, "We have to leave town."
4. Ivan asked, "Can't you put it off just one day?"
5. "No, I'm afraid we can't," said Earl.
6. "Then we'll just start over the following week," said Carmen cheerfully.
7. Jeannette said, "I bet no one else has done this."
8. "I sure hate to spoil our record," said Earl.
9. "Don't worry about it," said Ivan.
10. "Yes, everything will work out," said Jeannette.

Lesson 61, Using Commas (P. 88)

C.
1. Anthony, a grocery store owner, was planning for a busy day.
2. "Diane, would you open the store at 9 o'clock?" said Anthony.
3. "Of course, that's the time we always open," said Diane.
4. "Pierre, the chef at Elaine's, will be coming by," he said.
5. Kelly said, "Stephanie, I'd like some fresh peanuts."
6. "Yes, but how many pounds would you like?" answered Stephanie.
7. Ms. Harmon asked, "Martin, what kind of fresh fruit do you have?"
8. "Well, let me check what came in this afternoon," said Martin.
9. Alan, the butcher, had to wait on fifteen customers.
10. "I don't have time to wait, Alan," said Carol.
11. The manager, Juan, told everyone to be patient.
12. "Please, it will go quickly if you all take a number," said Juan.
13. "Yes, you're right as usual," said the crowd.
14. Martin, the produce manager, went behind the counter to help.
15. Well, they had sold all of their grapes and tomatoes before noon.
16. "We only have one bushel of green beans left," said Martin.
17. Mr. Loster bought cherries, bananas, and corn.
18. He was planning a special dinner for Sara, his wife.
19. Mr. Loster spent the afternoon cooking, baking, and cleaning.
20. Today, July 18, is her birthday.

D. Men, women, boys, and girls from across the nation participate in the Special Olympics. Because of this event, patterned after the Olympic games, boys and girls with disabilities have opportunities to compete in a variety of sports. The Special Olympics includes competition in track, swimming, and gymnastics. Volunteers plan carefully, and they work hard to ensure that the event will be challenging, rewarding, and worthwhile for all the participants. One of my neighbors, Chris Bell, once worked as a volunteer. "It was an experience that I'll never forget," he said.

Lesson 62, Using Quotation Marks and Apostrophes (P. 89)

A. **1.** "Wait for me," said Laura, "because I want to go with you."
2. "Kim, did you write an article about spacecraft?" asked Tom.
3. "Where is the manager's desk?" inquired the stranger.
4. Joanne asked, "What is Eric's address?"
5. David asked, "How long did Queen Victoria rule the British Empire?"
6. "Carlos, did you bring your interesting article?" asked the teacher.
7. "Good morning," said Cindy.
8. Doug asked, "Did Jim hurt himself when he fell?"
9. "The meeting begins in ten minutes," said Rico.
10. "Hoan, you're early," said Melissa.
11. "Come on," said the coach, "you'll have to play harder to win this game!"
12. Tony said, "I know you'll do well in your new job. You're a hard worker."

B. **1.** didn't; Sue's **2.** Haven't; Paul's **3.** didn't; Tom's **4.** employees'; didn't

Lesson 63, Using Colons and Hyphens (P. 90)

A. **1.** 2:10 **2.** you: **3.** 4:30 **4.** items: **5.** following: **6.** 8:00; 10:00 **7.** 3:00

B. **1.** garden-ing **2.** old-fashioned **3.** sign-up **4.** Twenty-seven **5.** daughter-in-law **6.** audi-torium **7.** well-known **8.** long-term

Review (P. 91)

A. The letters in bold should be circled.

1. **M**r. **J**. **C**. **M**oran owns a car dealership in **C**hicago, **I**llinois.
2. **J**esse decided to apply for a job on **T**uesday.
3. **W**ow, **M**r. **M**oran actually offered him a job!
4. **J**esse will start work in **J**une.
5. **J**esse is the newest employee of **M**oran's **C**ars and **V**ans.
6. **D**idn't he get auto experience when he lived in **M**innesota?
7. **H**e also got training at **D**unwoody **T**echnical **I**nstitute.
8. **J**esse took some computer courses there taught by **M**r. **T**ed **W**oods and **M**s. **J**ane **H**art.
9. **J**esse had only temporary jobs at **H**ighland **C**afe and **M**ayfield **E**lectronics for the last two years.
10. **S**ince **J**esse wants to be prepared for his new job, he checked out ***A**utomobile **T**echnology and the **A**utomobile **I**ndustry* from the **W**indham **L**ibrary.

B. **1.** After Jesse got the new job, his family, friends, and neighbors gave him a party.
2. Everyone brought food, drinks, and even some gifts.
3. Bob, Jesse's roommate, and Carmen, Jesse's sister, bought him a briefcase.
4. His mother and father bought him a new shirt and tie for his first day on the job.
5. His father congratulated him by saying, "Jesse, we are happy for you, and we wish you the best in your new job."
6. Jesse replied, "Well, I'm also very excited about it, and I want to thank all of you for the party and the gifts."

C. **1.** "How did you get so lucky, Jesse?" asked Mike.
2. "It wasn't luck," answered Jesse, "because I studied before I applied for this job."
3. "I didn't know you could study to apply for a job," said Mike, laughing.
4. "Mike, I read an employment guide before I applied," said Jesse.
5. "I have never heard of an employment guide!" exclaimed Mike.
6. "It's a great book," said Jesse.
7. "Jesse, I'd like to apply for a job at Moran's," said Mike.
8. Jesse replied, "Why don't you read my guide to prepare for the interview?"

Review (P. 92)

D. **1.** Joe King, Jesse's best friend, is the one who gave Jesse the employment guide to use for his interview at Moran's.
2. Jesse didn't know important interview skills.
3. The guide offered twenty-five helpful hints.
4. The guide suggested the following: dress neatly, be on time, be polite, and be enthusiastic.
5. Jesse also used the guide's suggestions for preparing a resume listing his work experience.
6. Jesse's list contained these items: his employers' names and addresses, dates of employment, and job descriptions.
7. The guide said Jesse should be a well-informed applicant, so he researched salesperson's duties and made a list of questions to ask.

8. Jesse's guide recommended getting to the interview early to have time to fill out the employer's application forms.
9. Jesse arrived at Mr. Moran's office at 3:45 for his 4:00 interview.
10. The interview lasted forty-five minutes, and Jesse was relaxed and self-confident when he left.
11. Mr. Moran's phone call the next day at 1:30 let Jesse know he had gotten the job.
12. Jesse needed to do the following: pick up a salesperson's manual, fill out employment forms, and enroll in the company's insurance program.

E. The letters in bold should be circled.

73 **E**. **R**iver **S**t.
Chicago, **IL** 65067
May 30, 2006

Dear **M**r. **M**oran:

I just wanted to thank you for offering me the salesperson's position with your company. **Y**ou mentioned in our interview that my duties would be the following: selling cars and vans, checking customers' credit references, and assisting customers with their paperwork. **I**'ve studied the automobile sales guide that you gave me, and **I** feel that **I**'m prepared to do a terrific job for **M**oran's. Thank you again. **I**'m looking forward to starting next **M**onday.

Sincerely,
Jesse **S**anchez

Using What You've Learned (P. 93)

A. The letters in bold should be circled.

720 **W**. **R**aven
Newland, **VA** 27890
May 4, 2006

Dear **S**irs:

On **M**ay 3, 2006, **I** received the compact disc player **I** had ordered from your catalog. **T**he following pieces were missing from the package: the battery pack, the high-quality headphones, and the adapter. **P**lease let me know what I should do about this. **W**ill you send the pieces, or should I return the whole package? **S**ince your motto is that customers' happiness is your goal, **I** thought **I** would let you know that **I**'m not very happy about this. **I**'ve ordered other things in the past. **T**hey were great. **W**hat happened to my order this time? **I**'m waiting anxiously for your answer.

Sincerely yours,
Bonita **W**illiams

B. The letters in bold should be circled.

478 **N**. **B**eacon
Trainor, **IN** 73210
June 1, 2006

Dear **M**s. **W**illiams:

Please excuse us. **T**his is awful! **D**o send the entire package back, and we will replace it. **H**ow can we apologize properly? **F**irst, we will send your new compact disc player special delivery so you will get it quickly. **S**econd, we will enclose a copy of ***S**ounds of the **N**ineties* for your pleasure. **W**e are sorry. **T**hank you for your past orders. **O**ur customers' happiness is our major goal. **W**e'll do everything we can to make sure that this order goes through properly. **P**lease let us know if everything's there. **W**e look forward to hearing from you.

Gratefully yours,
The **S**ound **T**eam

Using What You've Learned (P. 94)

C.

720 W. Raven
Newland, VA 27890
June 27, 2006

Dear Sound Team:

Hurray! My compact disc player arrived today, and it's great! Thank you. Now when I walk my dog, I can listen to a CD. Thank you also for *Sounds of the Nineties*. Can you believe it? I have a copy of *Tunes of the Eighties* and had planned to buy *Sounds of the Nineties*! Now I don't have to. That's great!

I also want to thank you for your courteous letter. I'm sure mistakes can happen to anyone. Everyone's quick action was greatly appreciated. Your letter and package arrived at 10:00 this morning. You're fantastic!

Sincerely,
Bonita Williams

Unit 5 Composition

Lesson 64, Writing Sentences (P. 95)

A. Discuss your answers with your instructor.

B. Discuss your answers with your instructor.

Lesson 65, Writing Topic Sentences (P. 96)

A. 1. Mario knew that having good questions was very important to a successful interview.
2. He wanted to include something about the history of the park.
3. Mario found out that the park was nearly as old as the town itself.

B. Discuss your answers with your instructor.

C. Discuss your answers with your instructor.

Lesson 66, Writing Supporting Details (P. 97)

A. The first sentence should be circled, and the remaining sentences should be underlined.

Mario asked Theresa to help him with the article. She would write out the tape-recorded interviews. She would also make suggestions for changes. Finally, they would both work on typing the article.

B. Discuss your answers with your instructor.

C. Discuss your answers with your instructor.

Lesson 67, Ordering Information Within a Paragraph (P. 98)

A. 1. Chronological; first; Then; Finally
2. Spatial; next to; left; top; down

B. 2
3
4
1

C. Discuss your answers with your instructor.

Lesson 68, Topic and Audience (P. 99)

A. 1. c **2.** d **3.** a **4.** b **5.** c **6.** b **7.** d **8.** a **9.** c or d **10.** b

B. 1. On Tuesday evening...
2. Discuss your answers with your instructor.
3. Discuss your answers with your instructor.

C. Discuss your answers with your instructor.

Lesson 69, Clustering (P. 100)

A. Discuss your answers with your instructor.

B. Discuss your answers with your instructor.

C. Discuss your answers with your instructor.

Lesson 70, Outlining (P. 101)

Discuss your answers with your instructor.

Lesson 71, Preparing Interview Questions (P. 102)

A. 1. Who **2.** What **3.** How or When **4.** Where **5.** Why **6.** When

B. Discuss your answers with your instructor.

C. Discuss your answers with your instructor.

Lesson 72, Writing Based on an Interview (P. 103)

1. no
2. Discuss your answers with your instructor.
3. Its facilities, which will include...
4. Discuss your answers with your instructor.
5. a small ice rink, meeting rooms, arts-and-crafts facilities, locker rooms with showers, and possibly a weight-lifting room

Lesson 73, Revising and Proofreading (P. 104)

A. The Berryton City Council approved plans today for construction of a new recreation center. Mayor June Booth said, "The center, to be located on the site of the current Adams Park, will provide Berryton residents with a variety of recreational programs." The center's facilities will include an indoor pool, two gymnasiums, arts-and-crafts facilities, and a small ice rink. Several meeting rooms will also be included for use by various organizations.

Lesson 73, Revising and Proofreading (P. 105)

B. ¶Representatives from severals community organizations attended the meeting to express their support of the recreation center. "Construction of this center is Long Overdue. Are members will now have a central place in which to meat, instead of crowding into each other's homes," said Milton Sayre, chairman of the berryton citizens' senior league.

¶ plans call for a groundbreaking ceremony on thursday, may 16, at 2:30, followed by a reception in adams park. ~~Construction is scheduled~~ mayor booth, supervisor john leland, and city council members will participate. all residents are invited to join them at the ceremoney.

Representatives from several community organizations attended the meeting to express their support of the recreation center. "Construction of this center is long overdue. Our members will now have a central place in which to meet, instead of crowding into each other's homes," said Milton Sayre, chairman of the Berryton Senior Citizens' League.

Plans call for a groundbreaking ceremony on Thursday, May 16, at 2:30, followed by a reception in Adams Park. Mayor Booth, Supervisor John Leland, and City Council members will participate. All residents are invited to join them at the ceremony.

Review (P. 106)

A. Discuss your answers with your instructor.

B. The following should be circled: **Phonograph records have changed over the years.** All the other sentences except "Edison also invented electricity." should be underlined.

C. Discuss your answers with your instructor.

D. Discuss your answers with your instructor.

Review (P. 107)

E. Discuss your answers with your instructor.

4, **Finally** 1, **Begin**
2, **Next** 3, **Then**

F. Discuss your answers with your instructor.

G. **1.** Discuss your answers with your instructor.
2. 4

H. Once the fog cleared, James drove to the airport to pick up his sister. When he got there, he discovered the plane was late. He asked the ticket person, "When will the flight from Mexico City arrive?" The person told him it would be another two hours.

Using What You've Learned (P. 108)

A. Discuss your answers with your instructor.

B. Discuss your answers with your instructor.

C. Discuss your answers with your instructor.

D. Discuss your answers with your instructor.

E. Discuss your answers with your instructor.

Using What You've Learned (P. 109)

F. Discuss your answers with your instructor.

G. Discuss your answers with your instructor.

H. One of the most important pieces of fire safety equipment is the smoke detector. The smoke detector continually monitors the air in your house. It sounds an alarm at the first sign of trouble. Fire officials consider smoke detectors one of the most effective, low-cost alarms available today.

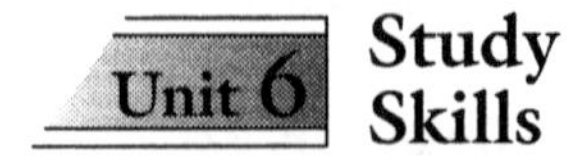

Study Skills

Lesson 74, Dictionary: Guide Words (P. 110)

A. The following words should be checked:

1. faster, fetch, flag, fancy, fertile, flame
2. impossible, incomplete, immense, indeed, improve, infect, imagine
3. rail, ranch, raw, raft, ramp, rate, rake

B. Words should be numbered to appear in the following order:

1. beach, bear, bedroom, believe, benefit, biography, blame, blend, blink, block, Guide words: beach/block.
2. department, depend, dessert, determine, difference, dine, discard, disease, district, disturb. Guide words: department/disturb.
3. face, faint, fair, family, finger, fire, flavor, flower, follow, free. Guide words: face/free.

Lesson 75, Dictionary: Syllables (P. 111)

A.

1. al-low-ance **11.** bril-liant
2. por-ridge **12.** ent-hu-si-asm
3. har-ness **13.** dra-mat-ic
4. ped-dle **14.** em-ploy-ment
5. char-ac-ter **15.** lab-o-ra-to-ry
6. hick-o-ry **16.** judg-ment
7. so-lu-tion **17.** king-dom
8. va-ri-e-ty **18.** rec-og-nize
9. tal-ent **19.** u-su-al
10. weath-er **20.** yes-ter-day

B. Answers will vary. Suggested:

1. vic-torious victori-ous
2. in-ferior inferi-or
3. quan-tity quanti-ty
4. sat-isfactory satisfacto-ry
5. se-curity securi-ty
6. pos-session posses-sion
7. ther-mometer thermome-ter
8. get-away geta-way

Lesson 76, Dictionary: Pronunciation (P. 112)

A. 1. 5 2. zh 3. ä 4. hw 5. ə 6. ü

B. 1. heel 2. ivy 3. they 4. letter 5. cape 6. retire 7. retreat 8. sap 9. down 10. new 11. height 12. noise 13. weight 14. diamond 15. iron 16. lead

Lesson 77, Dictionary: Definitions and Parts of Speech (P. 113)

1. cage, costume
2. cotton
3. cotton
4. cotton
5. an outfit worn in pretending to be someone else
6. Discuss your answers with your instructor.
7. Discuss your answers with your instructor.
8. Discuss your answers with your instructor.

Lesson 78, Dictionary: Word Origins (P. 114)

1. guppy
2. emotion
3. Old French and Old English
4. load
5. marathon
6. emotion; line; load
7. to move away; disturb
8. He introduced the fish to England.
9. from the Old English word *lad*
10. because a messenger once ran from Marathon to Athens to announce a victory over the Persians
11. load
12. line
13. emotion, line

Lesson 79, Using Parts of a Book (P. 115)

A. 1. index 2. title page 3. table of contents 4. copyright page 5. title page 6. copyright page

B. 1. Harcourt Achieve Inc. 2. 6 3. 18 4. inside back cover 5. 2006 6. 66 and 67 7. 95 8. 87 and 88 9. End Punctuation 10. 74, 75, and 76 11. 110 12. 8 13. 41

Lesson 80, Using Visual Aids (P. 116)

A. 1. 18; 22; 14; 4; 13
2. yes; no (The numbers on the graph are given only in increments of five.)
3. Friday
4. Tuesday
5. 38
6. Monday

Lesson 80, Using Visual Aids (P. 117)

B. 1. north
2. Loop 7
3. about 2 miles (about 3 km)
4. state
5. east/west
6. yes
7. 4
8. about 8 or 9 miles (about 12 or 13 km), depending on the route taken

Lesson 81, Using the Library (P. 118)

A. 1. 000–099 2. 500–599 3. 500–599 4. 100–199 5. 400–499 6. 600–699 7. 500–599 8. 000–099 9. 700–799 10. 800–899 11. 300–399 12. 900–999 13. 200–299 14. 000–099 15. 700–799

B. Discuss your answers with your instructor.

Lesson 82, Using a Card Catalog (P. 119)

A. 1. *Conserving the Atmosphere*
2. John D. Baines
3. Raintree/Steck-Vaughn, 1989
4. 363.73; 48
5. Air Pollution
6. yes

B. 1. subject 2. title 3. author 4. author

Lesson 83, Using an Encyclopedia (P. 120)

A. 1. Discuss your answers with your instructor.
2. 1888-1931
3. Voss, Norway
4. The University of Notre Dame
5. being the head coach of Notre Dame's football team.

B. 1. Discuss your answers with your instructor.
2. the west coast of the United States
3. coast or California redwood
4. It grows extremely tall.
5. 200 to 275 feet

C. Discuss your answers with your instructor.

Lesson 84, Using an Encyclopedia Index (P. 121)

1. 1
2. 68
3. no
4. cocktail, dip, pickle and relish, spread
5. main food or ingredient
6. acorn squash
7. almonds and stuffed celery
8. flour
9. appetizer
10. cheese ball
11. peanut flour

Lesson 85, Using a Thesaurus (P. 122)

A. **1.** difficult
2. puzzling, complex, awkward
3. complex
4. puzzling
5. awkward
6. simple, effortless
7. simple

B. **1.** complex **2.** awkward **3.** puzzling

C. Discuss your answers with your instructor.

Lesson 85, Using a Thesaurus (P. 123)

D. **1.** whisper **2.** describe **3.** argue **4.** chat **5.** discuss **6.** say **7.** grumble **8.** mention

E. Discuss your answers with your instructor.

F. **1.** glared **2.** roar **3.** matured **4.** gather **5.** knife **6.** opinion **7.** knot **8.** imagine **9.** knocked **10.** alarm **11.** drifted **12.** leave **13.** hid

Lesson 86, Using the *Readers' Guide* (P. 124)

1. Dave Berkman
2. *US News and World Report*
3. A. Comarow
4. *Television Quarterly*
5. television
6. 63–69
7. 115
8. November 1993
9. il.
10. October 1993

Lesson 87, Choosing Reference Sources (P. 125)

1. encyclopedia
2. *Readers' Guide*
3. atlas or encyclopedia
4. dictionary
5. almanac
6. atlas
7. thesaurus
8. dictionary
9. *Readers' Guide*
10. dictionary
11. encyclopedia
12. thesaurus
13. encyclopedia
14. *Readers' Guide*
15. almanac
16. dictionary

Lesson 88, Using Reference Sources (P. 126)

A. Discuss your answers with your instructor.

Lesson 88, Using Reference Sources (P. 127)

B. Discuss your answers with your instructor.

C. Discuss your answers with your instructor.

Review (P. 128)

A. **1.** export/extend
2. verb; noun; verb
3. 4; 2
4. **a.** exquisite
b. expose
c. exposition
d. express
5. express
6. Middle English, Middle French; Latin
7. Discuss your answers with your instructor.
8. exquisite

B. **1.** title page **2.** table of contents **3.** copyright page **4.** index **5.** copyright page **6.** title page

Review (P. 129)

C. **1.** west
2. state
3. about 4 miles (about 6 km)

D. **1.** activity
2. inactivity, inaction, motionlessness

E. **1.** "Make Them Truly Democratic"
2. *The Nation*
3. 688–702

F. **1.** atlas **2.** dictionary **3.** thesaurus **4.** encyclopedia **5.** almanac

Using What You've Learned (P. 130)

A. **1.** Discuss your answers with your instructor.
2. hu-mor
3. noun; verb
4. Discuss your answers with your instructor.

B. **1.** author card
2. 520.0
3. Stars and Planets
4. yes

C. **1.** the Cree, a Native American people
2. southwest into buffalo country
3. Native Americans

Using What You've Learned (P. 131)

D. **1.** Onward and Upward with the Arts: Letting It Be
2. Mark Hertsgaard
3. *New Yorker*

E. Discuss your answers with your instructor.

F. Chart information should be accurately shown on graph.

1. 40 **2.** 80 **3.** 1960 and 1990

G. **1.** 5 **2.** 877 **3.** families, grandparents

Final Reviews

Final Review, Unit 1 (P. 132)

1. S **2.** S **3.** A **4.** A **5.** S **6.** A **7.** A **8.** S **9.** A

1. by, plane, aunt
2. great, capitol
3. hair, paws, tail

1. a **2.** b **3.** b **4.** a **5.** b

1. S, C **2.** C, S **3.** P, S **4.** C, S **5.** P, S **6.** C, P **7.** P, C **8.** S, C **9.** C, S

Final Review, Unit 1 (P. 133)

1. I'm **2.** wouldn't **3.** don't **4.** I've **5.** you've **6.** isn't **7.** won't **8.** doesn't **9.** I'll **10.** they're **11.** hadn't **12.** there's

1. N **2.** – **3.** – **4.** + **5.** – **6.** – **7.** N **8.** + **9.** + **10.** N **11.** – **12.** N **13.** – **14.** +

Discuss your answers with your instructor.

1. knock my socks off
2. out like a light
3. flew off the handle
4. lit up the sky
5. let the cat out of the bag
6. down in the dumps
7. on cloud nine
8. on the fence

Final Review, Unit 2 (P. 134)

1. E; ! **2.** IN; ? **3.** IM; . **4.** D; . **5.** X **6.** D; . **7.** IM; . **8.** D; .

1. SS, CP, Steve/washed and...
2. CS, SP, Steve's sister and brother/helped him...
3. SS, SP, The sky-blue car/shone in the sun.
4. SS, SP, Steve/keeps his car...
5. CS, SP, Steve and his neighbor/work on...
6. SS, CP, Both young men/are taking...
7. SS, CP, The car/looks great...
8. CS, SP, Steve and his neighbor both/love that car.

1. Jason wasn't sure what to do, and Maria wasn't helping with her suggestions.
2. He listened to what Susan said, but her ideas just wouldn't work.
3. It was getting dark, and they needed to leave soon.
4. Jason had an idea, and Maria agreed with it.

IO DO
1. The store gave the contest winner a free trip.
IO DO
2. The coach bought his soccer team pepperoni pizzas.
IO DO
3. Tomás handed the taxi driver a generous tip.

Final Review, Unit 2 (P. 135)

Discuss your answers with your instructor.

The words in bold should be circled.

1. The paintings **we saw at the museum** were beautiful.; adjective clause
2. **Before Maria went to college**, she traveled for a year.; adverb clause
3. Employees **who work the night shift at the plant** receive extra pay.; adjective clause
4. Marla found her missing keys **when she was searching for her briefcase**.; adverb clause
5. The landlord remodeled our apartment **after we signed the new lease**.; adverb clause
6. Edgar Allan Poe was a famous poet **who wrote poems and short stories**.; adjective clause
7. The dresser **that we saw at the garage sale** was a valuable antique.; adjective clause
8. Carlos volunteered at the community center **because he liked helping children**.; adverb clause
9. We stopped delivery of the newspaper and the mail **since we were going away for a month**.; adverb clause
10. **Although my sister moved away**, we still talk on the phone three times a week.; adverb clause

Sentences will vary. Suggested:

1. The doctor who specializes in cancer research spoke to the medical students.
2. Mr. Burris will notify the office when he arrives at his destination.
3. The library where we do our research is closed for repairs all week.
4. The coal mine, which has been closed for safety reasons, will begin operating again next month.

1.–2. Discuss your answers with your instructor.

Final Review, Unit 3 (P. 136)

1. We (pron.) had grilled steak (n.), baked potatoes, and (conj.) a fresh (adj.) tossed salad for (prep.) dinner.
2. The exhausted (adj.) hikers quickly (adv.) set (v.) up their (pron.) tents and (conj.) went to sleep.
3. The Japanese (adj.) gardener pruned (v.) the young fruit (adj.) trees and rose bushes (n.) carefully (adv.).
4. Anthony (n.) tried very (adv.) hard to finish the mystery (adj.) novel, but (conj.) he (pron.) fell asleep.
5. The island's (adj.) tourists quietly (adv.) watched (v.) the glorious sunset (n.) until (conj.) it disappeared.

The words in bold should be circled.

1. **Gardening**, is
2. will receive, **swimming**
3. drove, **to fish**
4. has tried, **to throw**
5. chose, **to wait**
6. broke, **to steal**
7. has decided, **to move**
8. **winning**, was chosen
9. **dried**, smell
10. brought, **baked**
11. come, **to tell**
12. done, **reading**

The words in bold should be circled.

1. **brothers**, their
2. **bird**, it
3. **coach**, his

1. earlier
2. more expensive
3. tallest
4. fresher
5. saddest

Final Review, Unit 3 (P. 137)

Answers may vary. Suggested paragraph:

Manatees are mammals whose population is endangered. Also known as sea cows, manatees have dark gray skin, a very small head, poorly developed eyes that don't see well, and two front flippers. Their tails are large, rounded flippers. Manatees live in shallow, fresh water or saltwater and eat underwater plants. They live in the southeastern part of the United States, western Africa, South America, the Amazon, and the Caribbean Sea.

Manatees are very gentle animals. Rubbing muzzles is how they communicate. If alarmed, they make a chirping noise. By adulthood, they grow to between eight and fifteen feet and weigh nearly 1,500 pounds. Scientists studying an adult manatee have observed that it can eat about 100 pounds of plants in one day.

Manatees can clean waterways by eating vegetation before it blocks narrow passages. In some areas, manatees are encouraged to thrive so they will keep waterways free of plants. Boats and boat propellers are the worst enemy of the manatee. In a few places, people hunt them for meat, oil, and hides. This hunting has lead to the decline of the manatee population. However, in most areas, manatees are protected by law.

Final Review, Unit 4 (P. 138)

The first letter of the following should be circled and capitalized, and end punctuation should be added:

1. The; Nov.; Detroit; Michigan; .
2. Tom; How; Italian; ?
3. Dr.; Smith; Betsy; Ford; .
4. Wow; Betsy; American; Mr.; Lane; .
5. They; Japan; .
6. Tom; Are; Monday; ?
7. Mr.; Lane; No; I; Kyoto; Japan; .
8. Betsy; Tom; .

1. Yes, we have visited Japan, France, and Italy.
2. After we picked up Pepe, my poodle, from the groomer, we took him to the veterinarian.
3. Well, I think the judge showed compassion, integrity, and fairness in the courtroom.
4. Bill, the rehearsal is beginning, and we need you to join us now.
5. Belinda, my oldest sister, earns extra money by running errands, sewing, and cooking for our neighbor.
6. Jeff, please finish your report, and I will type it for you.

1. Tony said, "Meg, I saw your dog in Kevin's yard."
2. "Julio, the telegram is for you," called his brother.
3. Mr. Simpson asked, "What time does the softball game begin?"

4. "Ms. Ito," asked the reporter, "are you going to run for mayor?"
5. "Our company is on McNeil Road," replied the receptionist.
6. "You need to improve your defense," said Coach Díaz, "if you expect to win the big game."

Final Review, Unit 4 (P. 139)

1. I can't find the consultant's report anywhere.
2. The team's new uniforms weren't sewn properly.
3. Doesn't that store sell women's jewelry?
4. The horses' owner wouldn't sell them for any price.
5. Can't you pick up Stephanie's car for her at the repair shop?

1. Our meeting is at 1:30 this afternoon, and you need to remind the fol-lowing people: Jim Brown, Patricia West, Ann Tyler, and Jeff Ray.
2. My brother-in-law helped us move into our second-story apartment.
3. Between 1:00 and 5:00 yesterday, twenty-five people signed the sign-up sheet for the conference.
4. The well-known Italian restaurant specializes in the following foods: lasagna, grilled shrimp, veal, and spaghetti with meatballs.
5. My great-grandfather will be eighty-seven years old tomorrow.

The letters in bold should be circled.

3720 **W**. **A**nderson
Phoenix, **AZ** 37825
May 7, 2006

Ms. **J**ean **J**ackson
735 **W**. 79th **S**treet
Detroit, **MI** 14728

Dear **M**s. **J**ackson:

I want to enter my antique **F**ord, **B**etsy, in the Rally of the Americas, to be held **A**ugust 12, 2006. **P**lease send me any information **I** may need to register. **I** understand you only accept seventy-five entries. **A**m **I** too late? **I** was told to wait until **M**ay to inquire, so **I** hope there are still openings.

A friend who has entered in the past said this is the best rally of the whole year! **I**'m excited about entering. **M**y car is a 1910 classic in excellent condition. **I**t has won numerous awards over the years, and it is not ready to retire. **M**y wife and **I** are looking forward to the drive from our home in **A**rizona all the way to **D**etroit. **W**e're studying the book ***T**he **M**otor **C**ity* in anticipation of our visit. **I**'ll be waiting to hear from you.

Sincerely yours,
Dr. **L**ee **S**mith

Final Review, Unit 5 (P. 140)

1. In order to prove that shipwrecked sailors could survive in an open boat at sea, Dr. Bombard decided to conduct an experiment.
   Dr. Bombard discovered two very important things on his journey.
2. Answers may vary. Suggested: 4; 7
3. chronological
4. First; Then; Finally
5. Dr. Bombard's experiment
6. Discuss your answers with your instructor.
7. Discuss your answers with your instructor.
8. Discuss your answers with your instructor.

Final Review, Unit 5 (P. 141)

Discuss your answers with your instructor.

The birth of the island of Surtsey was a violent event.

¶Years ago there were Thousands of merry go rounds in the united states Many were made in new york. the carosel horses were hand painted and carved Each horse was difrent. now there are only a few hundred carousels left.

¶ the history of Carousels began in france. solders played a game on horseback Carousels were invented to help the practice for the game

Years ago there were thousands of merry-go-rounds in the United States. Many were made in New York. The carousel horses were hand-carved and painted. Each horse was different. Now there are only a few hundred carousels left.

The history of carousels began in France. Soldiers played a game on horseback. Carousels were invented to help them practice for the game.

Final Review, Unit 6 (P. 142)

1. b
2. 2; 3
3. Discuss your answers with your instructor.
4. to receive in return for work done
5. verb; noun
6. 1
7. ûrn; ûrth
8. earn
9. earth

1. index
2. title page
3. table of contents
4. copyright page

1. RG
2. D
3. E
4. AT
5. TH
6. E

Final Review, Unit 6 (P. 143)

1. south
2. about 1 mile (about 2 km)
3. east/west

1. Frank L. Tambo 2. 643.8 3. Macmillan

1. produce
2. verb
3. bear, yield, give, cause, make

1. M. Dane 2. 76–79 3. yes

Check What You've Learned (P. 144)

A. 1. S 2. H 3. A 4. H

B. jar

C. 1. S 2. C 3. P 4. C

D. 1. I would 2. do not

E. horrible

F. 1

G. The words in bold should be circled.

1. E; that, **is**
2. IM; (You), **read**
3. D; I, **am watching**
4. IN; Who, **wanted**

H. 1. CS 2. CP

I. 1. CS 2. I 3. RO

J. Dana gave her the box (DO) of chocolates [that someone had sent].

Check What You've Learned (P. 145)

K. The words in bold should be circled.

It was up to **Dr. Martinez** to decide how serious **Sharise's** illness was.

L. The words in bold should be circled.

Phoebe, **Diane's old-fashioned china doll**, is forty-one years old.

M. 1. past 2. future 3. present

N. 1. doesn't, drew
2. fallen, given
3. took, written
4. rang, chosen

O. 2

P. The words in bold should be circled.

1. SP, **they**
2. OP, **him**
3. PP, **His**
4. IP, **Nobody**

Q. The word in bold should be circled.

Robert behaved in his usual quiet manner.

R. 1. adjective
2. adverb
3. adjective
4. adverb

S. The words in bold should be circled.

He sat **in** a cafe **across** the street, although she had urged him to join them **at** the restaurant.

Check What You've Learned (P. 146)

T.

482 W. Franklin St.
Overhill, MT 80897
Aug. 22, 2006

Dear Ms. Muller:

I received the application you sent me, but these enclosures were not included: the aptitude test, the self-addressed envelope, and the postcard. Would you please send them as soon as possible? I want to complete everything just as you want it.

I'd like to confirm our appointment for Wednesday, September 14, at 3:15 P.M. I look forward to seeing you then and talking with you about the scholarship.

Yours truly,
Roy Thompson

U. 1. 3
2. 4
3. 5
4. 2
5. 1

V. 1

Check What You've Learned (P. 147)

W. Pluto is not only the smallest planet, it's also the farthest from the sun.

X. 1. noun
2. before
3. Latin
4. thoughtful
5. ro-tun-da

Y. 1. dictionary
2. card catalog
3. encyclopedia
4. *Readers' Guide*
5. atlas